Blood and Bone Marrow
Cell Culture

BLOOD AND BONE MARROW CELL CULTURE

by

H. Jackson Woodliff

M.B., Ph.D., M.R.C.P.E., M.C.P.A., M.C.Path., D.C.P., D.Path.

LONDON
Eyre & Spottiswoode
1964

first published 1964
© 1964 *H. Jackson Woodliff*
Type set by Gloucester Typesetting Co.
Printed in Great Britain
by T. H. Brickell & Son Ltd
Gillingham, Dorset

Contents

Chapter 4   Cultures of normal blood and bone marrow cells

Chapter 5 Cultures of abnormal blood and bone marrow cells

Chapter 6 The effect of nutrients and stimulants on cell cultures

Chapter 7   The effect of cytotoxic therapeutic agents on cell cultures

Chapter 8   Discussion

Illustrations

Plates

Preface

This monograph on cell culture is based on a review of the literature and on the author's personal experience of the subject. *In vitro* culture offers an attractive, though to some extent artificial, method of studying cells in which they are separated from their normal environment in the host and can therefore be subjected to experimental procedures. In recent years many advances have been made in culture techniques by workers in the fields of oncology, virology and cytogenetics. Haematologists have also been attracted by cell culture techniques since many of the problems in haematology are concerned with the normal or abnormal multiplication and maturation of blood cells. Many methods have been used and much useful information obtained. The results however, have, sometimes been conflicting and underline the fact that an ideal method of culture has yet to be developed. One of the major objectives of workers in this field has been to develop improved technical methods so that reproducible cultures suitable for quantitative studies of cell behaviour *in vitro* might be made. To this end the recent advances made by workers in other fields are reviewed with a view to their possible applications in haematology. The results of culturing both normal and pathological cells are described and the effect of physiological substances and stimulants on the cells considered. Particular emphasis centres on the study of therapeutic agents on blood and bone marrow cells *in vitro*. Antimetabolic, cytotoxic and steroid drugs and ionising radiations are used in the treatment of malignant disorders including those of haemopoietic tissues. Unfortunately the effect of such agents on the disease processes *in vivo* is not uniform. In some instances a remission is induced but in others the condition appears to be resistant to the treatment. By studying the effects of these agents on cells *in vitro* it is to be hoped that a prediction may be made as to their effect *in vivo*. The prospects for this and other future developments in the field are discussed.

I am grateful to the many individuals who have helped in my studies and in the preparation of this monograph. Dr F. G. J. Hayhoe supervised my studies at Cambridge University; many cell culturists in Britain and the United States of America allowed me to visit their laboratories, showed me their techniques and discussed mutual problems with me; other cell culturists who have corresponded with me, have helped with details and references; technical help has been given by Mr R. J. Flemans, Cambridge, England, Miss T. Minett, Oxford, England and Mr P. Onesti, Perth, Western Australia; my wife, Mary I. Woodliff, Kay O'Connor and Valerie I. L. Straker have given valuable secretarial assistance. Dr R. M. Bannerman read the monograph and made many useful suggestions. Mr M. Temple Smith and Miss Marjorie Norman of the publishers, Eyre & Spottiswoode, have been most helpful. Financial assistance for my studies has been given by the Elmore Fund of Cambridge University and the Lady Tata Memorial Fund. Mr R. Pendrill, Librarian, Royal College of Physicians, Edinburgh, helped with many of the references. The Academic Press Inc. have allowed me to reproduce Plate 1, S. Karger Basel/New York to reproduce Plate 2 and the Editor of the Texas Reports on Biology and Medicine to reproduce figure 6.

CHAPTER 1

Introduction to cell culture

Organ, tissue or cell culture may be defined as the maintenance alive of isolated parts of a multicellular organism *in vitro* for a considerable period of time. In most cultures of animal material, the portion being cultured, the explant, does not retain its normal histological structure in the absence of factors which control organ and tissue organisation *in vivo*. Cells migrate from the explants and one type commonly predominates. Similarly, if suspensions of cells are cultured a predominant type is soon found and there is no histological structure. These are called *cell cultures.*

A few methods have been developed to maintain organs *in vitro* without any outgrowth of cells; to these the term *organ culture* is applied.

Whilst the term *tissue culture* should, strictly speaking, be reserved for those techniques in which tissues are cultured, it is the term by which all these procedures are commonly known.

The term *maintenance*, which implies survival of some of the explanted material, should be distinguished from *growth*, which means an increase in the size of the cells or their multiplication. Some restrict the use of the term tissue culture to those preparations in which growth occurs, but the wider meaning is used here.

This monograph is concerned only with the *in vitro* culture of cells. Other techniques in which the cells of a species are cultured in the tissue of other species or different individuals of the same species have been commonly used. They form a separate subject, that of *in vivo* culture.

The period of time in which cells must be kept *in vitro* to constitute a culture is not easily defined, it depends rather on the purpose of the experiment. Those experiments or procedures which aim to preserve cells for future *in vivo* use, such as the storage of blood for infusion, and those which are concerned with tissue or cell extracts rather than whole cells, are excluded. Included are techniques in which the cells are maintained at or near body temperature and observed for changes in morphology, behaviour, or chemistry even if the culture is maintained for only a few hours.

HISTORY

Cell cultures might be said to date from the experiments of Schultze (1865), Loeb (1897), Jolly (1903) or Harrison (1907).

Schultze examined blood cells on the warmed stage of a microscope and observed their behaviour. He recognised four types of leucocytes and described the amoeboid movements and phagocytic activities of some of them.

Loeb carried out extensive experiments on the fate of epithelium embedded on agar and coagulated serum. His cultures were usually re-embedded on the surface or inside animals and were thus of the *in vivo* type; however, it appears from his writings that on some occasions the cultures were incubated *in vitro*. Although the results were not as good as *in vivo*, at least he had attempted *in vitro* cultures of the type we know today. He was interested in the fate of the epithelium, believing that it developed into connective tissue, leucocytes and red corpuscles.

Another early study was that of Jolly, who described his experiments with the leucocytes of newts. These he was able to keep alive and active *in vitro* for nearly a month. Furthermore, he actually observed mitosis of cells in preparations up to fifteen days old.

It is of interest to note that these pioneers were all interested in blood cells. However, their observations were isolated and the modern era of tissue culture is generally accepted as beginning with the experiments of Harrison, reported in 1907.

He explanted the medullary tubes of embryo frogs onto coagulated lymph and observed the actual growth of axones from the nerve cells. The next year plasma was substituted for lymph and the classical plasma clot technique developed.

Soon afterwards bone marrow was cultured. The first experiments published were those of Carrel and Burrows (1910d) who used the plasma clot technique. The Lewises (Lewis and Lewis, 1911a), using a nutrient agar as the medium, had cultured marrow in 1908 but the results were not published until 1911.

Since then many investigators have cultured blood and bone marrow cells, as well as cells from many other organs and tissues.

PRINCIPLES AND PROSPECTS

The aim of culturing cells outside the body is to isolate them from the controlling influence of the whole organism and to bring them into a suitable state for examination and experimentation. One of the first essentials for successful culture is to maintain the cells, at least at first, in an environment as closely resembling that of the parent organism as possible. Human cells must be incubated, usually at 37°C, kept moist and supplied with nutrients. Around these basic requirements, many different techniques of culture have been evolved. Special vessels, media and apparatus have been developed. In centres carrying out extensive work in this subject, a suite of rooms and special techniques of asepsis have been used (Parker, 1961; White, 1954; Scherer, 1955a; Paul, 1960). However with the introduction of antibiotics there has been some relaxation in the high standards previously required and it is now possible to carry out cell cultures in a general laboratory and with comparatively simple equipment. In fact some types of culture require little equipment other than that found in most medical laboratories. Such methods are therefore suitable for general use.

Cell cultures are used as a research technique in fundamental cytology, for example in the investigation of normal cell metabolism, as well as in a variety of other specialised fields. In oncology, studies have been made to see if differences can be detected between malignant and normal cells. The malignant transformation of normal cells either spontaneously or under the influence of oncogenic agents has also been studied.

In virology, cell cultures have been used as a 'medium' for the growth of virus, for the detection of virus, for the diagnosis of viral types and for fundamental studies on virus-cell reactions. The fields of oncology, virology and cell culture meet in studies of the effects of tumour viruses on cellular metabolism and morphology.

Recent advances in cytogenetics have been helped by cell culture studies. By using special procedures the chromosomes of cells undergoing mitosis in culture have been spread so as to be suitable for analysis of their numbers and morphology.

Turning to haematology, there are many problems which might be solved by using a really successful method of culture. Comparatively little is known about the factors which influence the multiplication and maturation of blood cells and the nature of the stem cell from which they are derived is still undecided. If it were possible to

B

isolate, identify and grow single cells, then the conditions suitable for multiplication or maturation might be studied. It might even be possible to mass produce mature cells for infusion into human recipients. Another potentially rewarding field is in the study of leukaemia. Can normal cells *in vitro* be transformed into leukaemic cells; how do leukaemic cells differ from normal cells? Can they be classified by cell culture techniques in such a manner as to give a reliable prognosis for the patient suffering from leukaemia? Can the effect of drugs on the cells inside the body be predicted from their effect on the cells *in vitro*? Can infective agents be isolated from the cells, and will cells in culture support the growth of added infective agents? The possibilities are enormous, but comparatively few have been satisfactorily realised.

CHAPTER 2

Methods of culture

The methods used for culturing organs, tissues and cells *in vitro* are classified in fig. 1. In each, the cells are incubated at a suitable temperature and supplied with nutrients. The methods differ in the nature of the immediate environment of the cells. The microenvironment of the cells in a suspension culture is completely fluid and the same for each cell. In the solid substrate cultures the cells have a variable microenvironment, being in contact with the substrate and often with each other as well as with the fluid nutrient. Conditions are not, therefore, uniform. Organ cultures form a separate group. Here the intention is to maintain the cells in contact with one another as they were *in vivo*. More importance is placed on histological and cytological integrity than on multiplication or maturation.

The types of vessels used vary in size from a microchamber formed by the capillary space between a glass slide and coverslip to a litre bottle (fig. 2). Chambers are generally used when direct microscopic examination is desired or the size of the explant is small. Tubes can be used when only low power microscopy is required, whereas dishes and bottles are generally used for larger scale cultures in which direct study of the individual cell is not desired.

The immediate environment of the cells contains a nutrient fluid, and in cell suspension cultures that is all. In solid substrate culture, the cells are also in contact with either an inert or a nutrient solid. This acts as a physical support for the cells, which may either lie loosely on the surface or become attached to the substrate.

The fluid bathing the cells is usually the main source of nutrition; as well as performing this important function, it provides hydration, a supply of essential ions and it assists in the control of the hydrogen ion concentration and the osmotic pressures of the system. Often essential macromolecules are also provided. Generally the fluid is designed to resemble body fluids; it usually consists of serum or some similar protein fluid and a balanced salt solution containing dextrose. Tissue extracts or mixtures of amino acids and vitamins are often added to encourage growth. In more recent years completely artificial media have been developed but only a limited number of cell strains can grow in such protein-free media. They may, however, be used with serum to form a complete medium (Appendix A, see also Chapter 6).

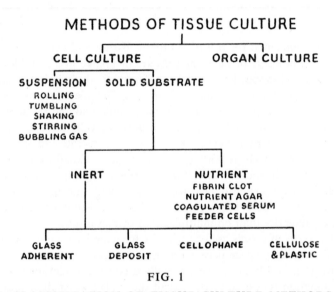

FIG. 1

A CLASSIFICATION OF TISSUE CULTURE METHODS

Solid substrates, which are divided into inert and nutrient groups, act as physical support for the cells which may lie either loosely on the surface or become attached to the substrate.

The inert substrates, which include glass, cellophane, cellulose and various plastics, act only in a physical sense. Nutrient substrates, which include fibrin clots, nutrient agars, coagulated sera and feeder cells may, as their name implies, also supply nutrients used by the cells.

Another factor in cell nutrition is a gas phase. Generally speaking, air or some other oxygen-containing gas is in equilibrium with the fluid phase of the cultures, thus allowing oxygen to reach the cells for respiration. Often the gas phase contains carbon dioxide and in some systems the concentration may be varied to control the hydrogen ion concentration. Nitrogen is usually used as an inert gas to make up the balance in experiments using differing concentrations of oxygen.

The length of time cell cultures can be kept viable varies with the cell types and methods used. For convenience, cultures of a few hours or days are called short-term cultures. Long-term cultures generally last for several weeks. Established cell strains are those which have been cultured continually *in vitro* for a year or more.

CELL SUSPENSION CULTURES

Cell suspension cultures are becoming increasingly popular in studies of the metabolism and multiplication of isolated cell strains and of the effects upon them of various agents.

They are ideally suited for such purposes because the cells are evenly distributed throughout a uniform environment.

Unfortunately, multiplication in such a system only occurs regularly in cell strains which have been previously established *in vitro* by other means.

Since the cells of the blood are in suspension one might think that such a method would suit them. Unfortunately, both blood and bone marrow cells soon die in such cultures, possibly due to mechanical damage, and the method is therefore only suitable for experiments of a few hours' duration.

Suspension cultures can be divided according to the methods which have been used in maintaining the suspension. These include rolling, tumbling, shaking, stirring, and bubbling gas.

Roller:

A rolling method was used by Earle *et al* (1954) for the culture of L strain mouse cells in suspension. The cells were placed in special culture tubes in an apparatus which rotated them horizontally at speeds of 18 to 2,400 revolutions per hour. The method has not been used for blood and bone marrow cells.

Tumbler:

A tumbling method in which the cells are rotated vertically so that a bubble of air or other gas flows through the medium at each revolution has also been described. It has been applied to an established strain of mouse lymphoblasts by Owen *et al* (1954), and to the L strain mouse fibroblasts by Siminovitche *et al* (1957). Preliminary experiments to determine its suitability for blood and bone marrow cell cultures have been discouraging. Cells in glass-stoppered pyrex

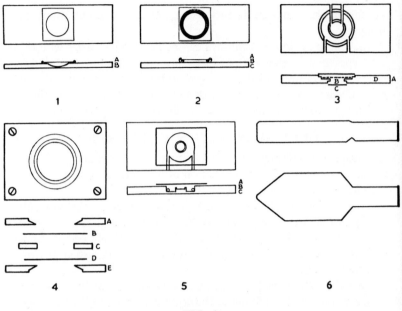

FIG. 2

CULTURE VESSELS

1 *Depression slide* (Harrison, 1907).

The plasma clot culture is prepared on a coverslip, which is then inverted over the depression in a glass slide; the coverslip is sealed to the slide with paraffin.

2 *Glass or metal ring chamber*

This is similar to (1). The plasma clot is prevented from coming into contact with the slide, which does not contain a depression, by means of a glass or metal ring.

3 *Modified Harris chamber* (Woodliff, 1958a).

This chamber, which is made of non-toxic plastic material, consists of two compartments, the lower being smaller than the upper; access to them is obtained through drill holes which can be closed by polythene plugs. They are separated by a removable coverslip, indicated in the diagram by the dotted line.

The coverslips are sealed in position with paraffin and cells inoculated into the lower chamber. After they have become adherent to the bottom coverslip, the middle coverslip may be removed; the upper chamber can then either be used to contain a gas phase, or to contain fresh medium which will equilibrate with that in the lower chamber.

4 *Rose Chamber* (Rose, 1954).
This multipurpose tissue culture chamber consists of two stainless steel plates, two large coverslips and a central rubber gasket. The plates are joined by screws and the chamber inoculated by means of hypodermic needles inserted through the rubber. Care must be taken to see that the rubber is non-toxic.

It is usually used for glass substrate cultures, without a gas phase. However it can be adapted to other types of culture, including serum agar cultures (Woodliff, 1958b).

5 *Pulvertaft chamber* (Pulvertaft and Weiss, 1957).
This chamber, which is made of non-toxic plastic material, was especially designed for serum agar cultures. The solid substrate is placed in the central well with the inoculum on top of it. The chamber is then closed by a coverslip which is sealed with paraffin wax. Fluid and gas phases can be introduced through the drill holes, which are closed by polythene plugs.

6 *T-flasks* (Earle and Highouse, 1954).
These flasks were introduced for replicate glass substrate cultures, but can also be used to contain small coverslips bearing plasma clot cultures.

7 *Saunders tubes* (Woodliff, 1958a).
These inexpensive light glass tubes can be used for glass substrate cultures. The thin neutral glass has reasonable optical properties allowing low but not high power microscopical examination of living cells to be made.

8 *Porter flasks* (Porter, Claude and Fullam, 1945).
These flasks were designed to fit into a rack for roller tubes so that plasma clot cultures could be kept healthy for a longer time than is possible with a slide technique. The cultures on coverslips are placed in the bottom of the flask and held in position by a thin plasma clot. After one or two days 1 ml of nutrient fluid is added and replenished as necessary.

9 *Carrel flasks* (Carrel, 1923).
These flasks were introduced by Carrel for plasma clot cultures. The advantages over slide cultures are that tissues can be maintained for several months, fluid medium can be added, and the gas phase controlled. The long neck discourages contamination with bacteria.

Flasks with good optical properties can be obtained suitable for medium power microscopy of the cells.

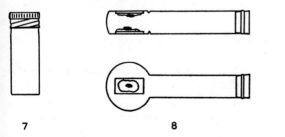

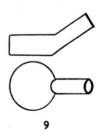

7   8   9

10 *Petri dishes*

Petri dishes can be used for glass substrate cultures, provided they are incubated in a moist atmosphere containing carbon dioxide to control the pH. They have been used more particularly by Puck (Puck, *et al*, 1956) to grow cell colonies from single cells, a process called cloning.

11 *Test tubes*

These can be used for either glass substrate cultures or plasma clot cultures.

12 *Gradient slide culture method* (Osgood and Krippaehne, 1955).

In the original technique which is illustrated, a glass slide (2.5 x 7.5 cm.) was placed in a 1-pint french square bottle, to which was added 170 ml of cell suspension. Gradient factors were worked out for each cell type (see text page 15).

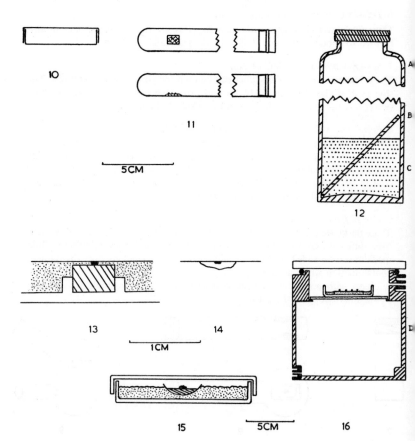

13 *Detail of serum agar culture*

Such a culture may be set up in the chamber illustrated in figs. 2.4 and 2.5. The serum agars (diagonal lines) is contained in the perspex and the inoculum (black dot) placed on top. It is flattened by a coverslip and surrounded by a thin layer of fluid medium (stippled).

14 *Detail of plasma clot culture*

This type of culture may be set up in the glass slides illustrated in fig. 2.1 and 2.2, or in the flasks illustrated in fig. 2.6, 2.8 and 2.9, or in the tube, fig. 2.11. The inoculum (black dot) on a coverslip is held in position by a plasma clot formed by the interaction of one drop of plasma and one drop of embryo extract. A fluid phase may be added if desired.

15 *Organ culture* (Strangeways and Fell, 1926).

The portion of organ being cultured is placed on top of a plasma clot contained in a watch glass. The watch glass rests on a pad of moistened cotton wool in a large petri dish. The plasma clot can be replaced by lens paper or rayon net floating on a liquid medium.

16 *Organ culture using Trowell chamber* (Trowell, 1959).

In this technique, portions of organs are placed on a perforated metal grid, and kept moist by capillarity from the surrounding medium. The culture dish is placed in a larger chamber which can be perfused with any gas phase desired.

test tubes were rotated on a disc at an angle of 45° to the horizontal on an apparatus made from parts of a gramophone with disc speeds of 33 and 45 revolutions per minute. The cell counts invariably decreased and morphological studies showed considerable cell damage.

Shaker:

Extending their studies of cell suspension cultures, Earle's group (Earle, *et al*, 1956) reported upon the use of a Brunswick shaker with speeds of up to 13,600 revs per hour in which cells were maintained in suspension by the shaking action. They obtained a luxuriant growth of three cell types, namely clone L 929, clone 1469 liver epithelium and a HeLa strain cervical carcinoma.

Unfortunately blood and bone marrow cells do not grow when shaken. Osgood and Brownlee (1937) mention that they tried shaking their bone marrow cell cultures without any noticeable benefit over those not shaken.

Others have also used such cultures but usually only for short-term experiments (Norris and Majnarich, 1948 a and b; Biesele and

Berger, 1950; Clemmesen and Plum, 1952). They are valuable for metabolic studies and can be used to measure cell respiration (Laszlo *et al*, 1958; Woodliff, 1962).

Stirrer:

A recent development has been the introduction of a method of keeping cells in suspension by means of a glass stirrer. Danes (1957) has perfected the technique for the culture of L strain mouse fibroblasts. The method is of great interest as a possible means of continuously growing cells by periodically harvesting and renewing the medium. Thus a constant supply of cells for virus studies could be provided. Attempts to apply the method to HeLa cells have been made but an increasing population was not obtained (Craven, 1958). The method has not yet been applied to blood and bone marrow cells.

Bubbler:

Plum (1947a) described a complex apparatus based on the one originally described by Osgood and Muscovitz (1936) in which the cells were kept in suspension by bubbling gas through the culture. Bone marrow cells were placed in a semi-permeable membrane which was surrounded by nutrient fluid. In Osgood's apparatus the cells were apparently deposited on the surface of the plastic; in Plum's however, they were prevented from sedimenting by the continuous movement of a current of air or other gas mixture introduced through a tube dipped in the culture. The method does not appear to have been used extensively as there is only one report in the literature (Plum, 1947b) of studies carried out with the apparatus.

SOLID SUBSTRATE CULTURES

The early methods of culture used solid nutrient substrates such as fibrin clots, coagulated sera and nutrient agars. More recently it has been realised that although many cells may need a solid upon which to support themselves, it does not itself have to be a nutrient. Solid substrate methods can, therefore, be divided into those utilising an inert substrate and those utilising a nutrient substrate.

Inert substrate cell cultures:

Of the inert substances, by far the most frequently used has been glass. Hard glass provides an ideal surface for cells and its transparency has obvious advantages. The use of cellophane is advised for certain cell types as growth may occur in greater profusion than

PLATE 1 CULTURED BONE MARROW CELLS

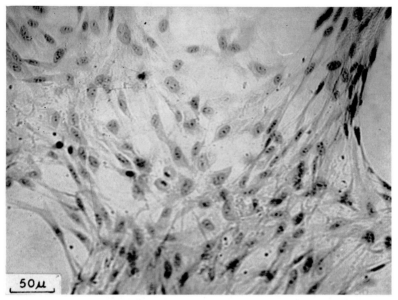

1a Sheet of fibroblast-like cells in a fifteen-day Saunders tube culture of bone marrow cells. An anaphase is present towards the bottom left. Fixed and stained by Leishman's stain.

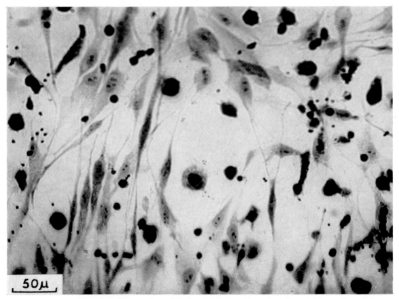

1b Large granular and fibroblast-like cells in a nine-day Saunders tube culture of bone marrow cells. Fixed and stained by Leishman's stain.

PLATE 1 CULTURED BONE MARROW CELLS

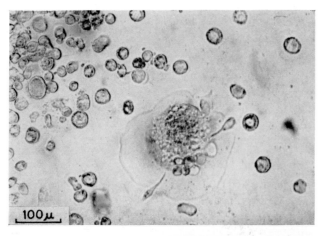

1c Megakaryocyte and large granular cells in a seven-day Saunders tube culture of bone marrow cells. Living cells photographed with ordinary illumination

1d Fibroblast-like cells growing out of a small fleck of bone marrow in a twelve-day Saunders tube culture. Living cells photographed with ordinary illumination.

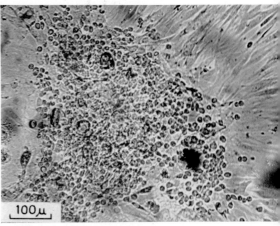

1e Fibroblast-like cell in a five-day Rose Chamber culture. Living cell photographed with phase contrast illumination.

on glass. Occasionally other substrates have been used for special purposes. For example, cells cultured on formvar films have been used for electron microscopy. It is important to realise that two sets of conditions may occur in inert substrate cultures. The cells may adhere to the substrate or they may merely become sedimented on it without any intimate connection. Sometimes a culture contains cells of both types.

Glass substrate adherent cultures

In long-term cultures only cells which adhere to the glass remain, as any loose cells are removed when the medium is changed. Depending upon the type of experiment the cultures may be carried out in chambers, tubes, flasks or dishes.

Chambers: An early account of such a culture was given by Lewis and Lewis (1911b); they placed small fragments of tissue in a chamber made by a slide, a coverslip and a ring of vaseline. Cells grew out along the glass. Recently the method has been further developed and used, especially when direct microscopy has been needed. Cells in suspension are introduced into a chamber where they settle and adhere to the glass which forms the floor. Rose (1955), for example, has used this method for studying HeLa cells. Such experiments have usually been limited to a few hours or days with no provision for a gas phase. However, Harris and Barclay (1955) in a study of rabbit macrophages provided for a gas phase and other authors have arranged methods for perfusion of such cultures (Richter and Woodward, 1955; Woodliff, 1958b). The method has been applied to blood and bone marrow cells (Woodliff, 1958a). Whilst the general pattern of cultures is rather irregular in tissue culture chambers it does allow high power microscopy (Plate 1a). Klein (1959) has used a similar method in a study of human foetal lymphocytes.

Tubes: Where large cell numbers are being studied or where only low power microscopy is required, it is more convenient to culture cells in tubes. Cells in suspension are allowed to settle on the floor of the tube to which they adhere; after several hours the fluid and gas phases may be changed without loss of cells. Sometimes the fluid phase is kept continuously in motion by placing the tube on a rolling apparatus (Ehrmann and Gey, 1953) but usually the tubes are stationary and the medium partially renewed at regular intervals. Many cell types, such as HeLa cells and human amnion cells are cultured in this way.

Studies of blood and bone marrow cells by this method have been made using small tubes (Woodliff, 1958a). The method allows of reasonably good low power microscopy (Plates 1a, b, c and d).

Flasks and dishes: Large numbers of cells can be grown in flasks and dishes which are used for this purpose and for certain specialised studies. Usually they are not suitable for direct microscopy and other means have to be used for cytological examination; for example, a coverslip may be placed inside the vessel and removed later for study. Otherwise they resemble tube cultures. Lewis and Lewis (1911b) used such a method to grow cells in petri dishes. They found that cells from pieces of tissue often grew down to the bottom of the dish and became firmly adherent to the glass. In more recent times an advance has been made by Puck and his colleagues (Puck and Marcus, 1956; Marcus *et al*, 1956), who are able to grow colonies from single cells in petri dishes. Flasks have been used for blood and bone marrow cell cultures by various workers. Weiss and Fawcett (1953) cultured chicken macrophages in Porter flasks containing coverslips. Others have used Carrel flasks (McCulloch and Parker, 1956) and large prescription bottles (Berman *et al*, 1955) to culture cells of haemic origin. Carrel flasks have also been used for human bone marrow cell cultures, but are less convenient than small tubes.

Glass substrate deposit cultures

When suspensions of cells are allowed to settle in a glass container they deposit on the floor. Some cells adhere to the glass whilst the others lie on the glass without intimate contact or lie upon one another. Cultures of this kind have been extensively used in the culture of blood and bone marrow cells but have not been widely applied to other cell types, possibly because the latter grow better when adhering to the substrate. Osgood and Brownlee (1937) introduced this method for bone marrow cell culture. Both they and Israels (1940a), Gunz (1948a), Hoogstraten (1949) and Smith (1952) who have used similar techniques, ignored the possibility of cells becoming adherent to glass; a factor which must be taken into account in any quantitative assessment. Later workers, including Cairns and Lajtha (1948), Lajtha (1952) and Thomas (1956) avoided this by siliconing glass culture vessels. Cells in such cultures may be resuspended in the medium by shaking.

Whilst the same basic method has been employed by the various authors mentioned above, minor variations in technique regarding the type of culture vessel, the depth of medium, the cell concentration and the form of sampling have been described.

The method is suitable for blood cells which are already in suspension. With bone marrow cells there are difficulties in obtaining an even dispersion of the cells in the medium. This has led to wide variation in the cell counts of replicate cultures obtained by some workers (Thomas, 1956 and personal experience), making quantitative evaluation of the cultures difficult. Other workers have not experienced this difficulty and have been able to achieve results sufficiently consistent to allow of quantitative assessment of the cultures (Lajtha, 1952).

An ingenious development of the glass substrate culture was the gradient slide technique of Osgood and Krippaehne (1955). They placed a 3×1 inch glass slide at an angle in a square jar. A suspension of leucocytes in a suitable medium was added and the cells became deposited, some on the glass slide, others on the floor of the jar (fig. 2.12).

Osgood and Krippaehne found that conditions suitable for each of the blood cell types were present at different depths in the cultures. From this they worked out gradient factors (cell count per cu.mm in thousands multiplied by the depth in centimetres) for each cell type, which were used to determine the number of cells and depth of inoculum of subsequent flask cultures. Attempts by the present author to confirm the presence of 'gradients' in such cultures failed. The success of Osgood and his colleagues in the isolation of established cell strains from blood and bone marrow cells previously ascribed to this technique may also have been due to their use of phytohaemagglutinin (see p. 77). The 'gradient' principle can be used on a small scale using coverslips or small glass slides in universal containers. Personal experience of such cultures has shown that they fare no better than those in which cells are deposited on the floor of the container.

Cellophane substrate cultures

Evans and Earle (1947; Earle, 1951) introduced the use of perforated cellophane sheets which were placed in Carrel flasks, with a suitable medium. Incubation with cells under the cellophane led to a much better growth of normal and sarcomatous fibroblasts than were obtained on glass alone. The cells actually adhered to the cellophane. The method has been applied to human monocytes by Goldstein and McCormack (1957).

Other inert substrate cultures

Attempts by the Author to culture bone marrow cells soaked into a cellulose sponge were unsuccessful. Only fibroblast-like cells were found in sections of the cultures after incubation for one or more weeks.

Nutrient substrate cell cultures:

In an attempt to reproduce as nearly as possible the conditions *in vivo*, early *in vitro* cultures were made on or in solid nutrient substrates such as coagulated serum, fibrin clots and nutrient agars. Cultures of this type are still in extensive use today, although usually with some modification, such as the addition of a fluid phase. Their advantage lies in the fact that many types of material can be cultured in this way when other methods fail. They are often used for the primary isolation of cells which can subsequently be cultured in other ways. The disadvantage lies in the difficulties of evaluating the culture in the presence of biological fluids of variable composition. The most extensively used medium is the fibrin clot. Others include nutrient agars, coagulated sera and feeder cells (fig. 1).

Fibrin clot cultures

Harrison (1907) introduced the fibrin clot method. He studied the medullary tubes of an embryo frog which he kept alive in a hanging drop of coagulated lymph. The work interested Burrows (1910) who visited Harrison's laboratory to learn the technique, which he subsequently improved by substituting chicken plasma for frog's lymph as a source of the fibrin clot. The technique employed consists in placing a carefully isolated fragment of tissue in a drop of uncoagulated plasma and adding a drop of chick embryo extract on a cover glass. 'The cover glass is inverted and sealed to a hollow slide and the preparation is incubated at 39°C. The plasma immediately coagulates about the tissues and holds the fragment firmly in a fixed fibrin network' (fig. 2.14). Since then, the method has been extensively used and is still a standard practice.

Many modifications have been made to the original method, such as the use of a special slide which allows the fibrin clot to be removed and washed in nutrient (Maximow, 1929), and the adaptation of the method in various chambers which can contain a static or perfusing fluid phase (Buchsbaum and Kunz, 1954). The fibrin is usually derived from either natural or heparinised plasma which is clotted with embryo extract. Ebeling (1921a) used a solution of fibrinogen in an attempt to get more consistent results.

Fibrin clot cultures in hanging drops in slides or chambers are rather restricted and so some authors have used tubes and flasks. This usually means that microscopic examination, if possible at all, is limited to low power. In some experiments, however, slides or coverslips are placed in larger vessels and removed periodically for examination. The method has been extensively used and innovations have been made from time to time. Carrel (1923; fig. 2.9) introduced flasks that bear his name for such cultures. Later roller tubes (Gey, 1933) and flasks (Porter *et al*, 1945; fig. 2.8) were introduced so that the solid phase could be continuously bathed in fluid.

Another innovation has been the introduction of a third dimension by using a sponge matrix to hold the inoculum and the fibrin coagulum (Leighton, 1951).

Fibrin clot cultures of blood and bone marrow cells have been studied by many workers. The method was first used for these cells by Carrel and Burrows (1910c), who cultured a variety of organs including the marrow of a cat, and many workers have subsequently used similar methods of studying haemopoietic cells (Avroroff and Timofeevsky, 1914 and Verrati, 1928). In more modern times the method has been developed for the culture of human bone marrow by the Italian school (Fieschi and Astaldi, 1946a).

Nutrient agar cultures

Some of the earliest cultures were carried out in nutrient agar. Weil (1912) used such a medium in preference to plasma for epithelium cultures, and Smythe (1914) used an egg agar for chick tissue cells.

Bone marrow was cultured in a nutrient agar as early as 1908. Lewis and Lewis (1911a) wrote, 'In 1908 working under Dr Max Hurtman . . . , in Berlin, one of us found that bone marrow from the guinea pig formed a membrane-like outgrowth with mitotic figures on the surface of nutrient agar. This agar was a modification of one used at the Institute for the cultivation of amoeba. In the place of distilled water a modification of Ringers solution was substituted.' Ingerbrigtsen (1912) used a medium of serum and 2 per cent agar to culture adult guinea pig femoral marrow on a coverslip using a hanging drop technique. The use of serum agar was reintroduced in modern times by Pulvertaft (Pulvertaft and Jayne, 1953). In Pulvertaft's original technique a small square of agar was placed on a 3 × 1 inch slide. The inoculum on the agar was topped with a coverslip and sealed with paraffin. (fig. 2.13). Later special chambers were developed (Pulvertaft and Humble, 1956; Pulvertaft *et al*, 1956;

Pulvertaft and Weiss, 1957; fig. 2.5) in which a fluid and a gas phase could be in contact with the agar. A modification using a Rose chamber and allowing perfusion has also been described (Woodliff, 1958b).

Recently, both serum agar (Pulvertaft and Humble, 1956; Woodliff, 1961) and dextrose agar (Odom and Reisner, 1959) have been used for the culture of blood and bone marrow cells.

Feeder cell cultures

Cells which will not 'grow' by themselves can sometimes be cultured in the presence of other cells which 'feed' them. The 'feeder' cells as they are called, probably supply necessary metabolites for the more fastidious cells; they may, however, also act by removing toxic metabolic products, or in a mechanical way. Bichel (1939, 1952) first used such a method for culturing mouse lymphoblasts; he used mesenchymal cells as a support. De Bruyn (1949a) and the Kielers (Kieler and Kieler, 1954) have used similar methods for mouse tissues. Kieler (1955) tried to culture human leukaemic cells by this method but was unsuccessful.

Puck *et al* (1956) developed a technique using living but irradiation-inhibited feeder cells. This allowed them to grow clones of other cells upon the feeder layer. The irradiation-inhibited cells could not multiply and therefore did not contaminate the new colonies.

Brooke and Osgood (1959) have used the method to establish strains of human blood cells. They added new cells to previously well established cell cultures such as the Oregon J111. Since the feeder cells were not irradiated, interpretation of the findings in such a mixed culture is difficult. However, the method is a significant advance and it is to be hoped that confirmation of its value in the isolation of cell strains from peripheral blood will soon be forthcoming (see p. 57).

ORGAN CULTURES

Organ culture techniques introduced by Strangeways and Fell (1926; Fell, 1951; fig. 2.15) have been the subject of several improvements in recent years. Trowell (1952, 1954, 1959) replaced the plasma clot of the original method by cotton wool and later by lens paper supported on tantalum gauze; the cultures were kept moist by capillarity. Chen (1954) used lens paper floating on a liquid medium. He cultivated various organs of the foetal rat which grew and differentiated; however he made no mention of bone marrow. Trowell enclosed the whole of his cultures in a 'perspex' brand polymethyl-methacrylate chamber through which a gas mixture flowed (fig. 2.16). He obtained good results in the maintenance of rat lymph nodes, but results with bone marrow have been disappointing (Trowell, 1956, 1958). Practically all the haemopoietic cells died within three days, but the reticular cells survived for quite a long time. Various additions to the medium, different oxygen tensions and combined cultures with other organs were tried. In order to circumvent mechanical trauma, small plates of bone (rat femur) which had fragments of marrow attached were also cultured. None of these procedures produced any better results.

CHAPTER 3

Observation and evaluation of cell cultures

The methods used for observing and evaluating cell cultures vary according to the type and purposes of the experiment. For convenience they can be divided into those concerned with cell survival and metabolism with evidence of growth, including cellular maturation and transformation, and with the general pattern of the cultures.

CELL SURVIVAL

Cell survival is a fundamental requirement of a successful method of culture. Usually the whole or part of the culture is examined periodically for signs of life. These include cellular motility, alteration in cellular outline, intracellular movements, evidence of metabolic activity and morphological integrity.

Motility:
Cells which are actively motile are alive and usually healthy. Unfortunately, this criterion is only applicable to cells which are naturally motile and is limited to certain types of cultures. It is best suited to cultures in chambers where high power microscopy can be used. This type of observation is helped by the use of phase contrast illumination; other techniques which have been used include the use of vital stains, dark ground illumination and interference microscopy. Better optical results, and therefore more accurate observations, can be made in the absence of a solid nutrient substrate; of the solid substrates, agar media are generally clearer than fibrin clots. Studies of cell motility can be greatly helped by the use of time lapse cine-photomicrography (Pomerat *et al*, 1954). Studies of this type have been applied to blood and bone marrow cells by various authors (Rich *et al*, 1939; Pulvertaft and Humble, 1956; Lapin and Horonick, 1956; Woodliff, 1958a, 1961).

Alteration of cell outline:

Some cells are not progressively motile and others, whilst motile on occasions, may still be alive without showing this property. Careful observation of such cells often reveals that the outline of the cell is altering, a portion of cytoplasm being extended and then perhaps withdrawn. These observations require high power microscopy aided by phase contrast or dark ground illumination. Cells showing such movement are alive; however some alterations in cellular outline such as severe cytoplasmic bubbling may be terminal events heralding cell death.

Intracellular movements:

Some cells, whilst not showing any definite progressive motility of alteration of cell outline, may contain moving granules or other organelles. These movements, the result of cytoplasmic streaming, are definite and slow and should not be confused with the Brownian movement of cell particles seen after dilution of the cytoplasm by imbibed fluid.

Morphological integrity:

Direct microscopical examination of living cells is not possible in many types of culture and even in suitable cultures it is often omitted. Many workers have been content with the examination of fixed and stained cells recovered from the culture. These cells are not, of course, alive; what has to be deduced is the prefixation state of the cells, both with regard to viability and health. Generally speaking dead cells undergo fairly rapid autolytic changes and for this reason morphological integrity has often been regarded as sufficient evidence of prefixation viability. Whilst this may be valid in many cases, the criterion lacks the accuracy of direct observation. Many of the observations on blood and bone marrow cell cultures have been based on stained films or sections and whilst in most cases intact cells may be assumed to have been alive in the cultures, many show various signs of degeneration short of obvious disintegration. The prefixation viability of such cells must often be in doubt and conclusions based on the results of such observations may be misleading. The method has however the great advantage of being applicable to all types of culture, and so is still extensively used.

Differential and quantitative cell survival studies:

If different cell types can be recognised in the cultures, it may be possible to obtain a qualitative or semi-quantitative measurement of their relative survival times. Quantitative studies, however, are difficult because total cell counts are usually impractical and many cells present may defy classification. This defect is important in studies of agents having only a mild effect on the culture which may go undetected.

CELL METABOLISM

Evidence that cells in culture are alive may be obtained from a study of some of their metabolic processes. Whilst enzyme systems may continue to catalyse some vital chemical process for some time after cell disintegration, continuing and sustained metabolic activity is good evidence of cellular viability. Many of these processes can be observed qualitatively and some are suitable for quantitative studies.

Energy production:

Cellular energy is produced by the breakdown of glucose. This occurs in two stages; in the first, glucose is broken down to pyruvate (which may be converted to lactate) with the release of two high energy phosphate bonds. This process is called glycolysis; if it takes place in the absence of oxygen it is called anaerobic glycolysis, and if oxygen is present it is called aerobic glycolysis.

In the second stage, which requires oxygen, the pyruvate molecules are oxidised to carbon dioxide and water. Each molecule of glucose gives rise to two molecules of pyruvate, and the breakdown of these releases thirty-eight high energy phosphate bonds. The complete oxidation of glucose to carbon dioxide and water is called respiration and is much more efficient in energy production than glycolysis. (The term respiration is sometimes used to include all reactions which release energy; here it is restricted to mean oxygen consumption used in the oxidation of glucose and its products.) Both respiration, which is a feature of most cells, and aerobic glycolysis, which is a characteristic feature of embryonic and malignant cells and many cells in culture, can be measured.

Acid production:

Glycolysis results in the presence of pyruvic and lactic acids. These may produce a change in the hydrogen ion concentrations (pH) of the medium. Since most cultures are buffered, considerable acid is required to produce such a change, which is usually detected by the phenol red indicator included in most media. In actively growing cultures there is usually a gradual change from a pH of 7.4 down to pH 6.8 or so over a few days. Absence of such a change in virus infected cultures, when it is present in controls, indicates a cyto-pathic effect. The production of acid is a fair indication that cellular metabolism is active, but the reverse is not necessarily true as the hydrogen ion concentration may be stabilised by buffers or the loss of carbon dioxide or there may be too few cells to affect it. This parameter is therefore too crude to be of value in fine cytological work. Lactic and pyruvic acid production can also be measured chemically: in cultures incubated in an atmosphere lacking oxygen (usually nitrogen with some added carbon dioxide); this gives a measure of the anaerobic glycolysis. This is abbreviated to Q_A^{N2} the N_2 indicates the atmosphere of nitrogen and the A acid produced. In cultures incubated in an atmosphere containing oxygen (usually air or an oxygen carbon dioxide mixture) acid production measures aerobic glycolysis. This is abbreviated to Q_A^{O2}.

Oxygen uptake:

Oxygen uptake by cells is a measure of their respiration, and this is abbreviated to Q_{O_2}. It has been frequently measured in studies of cells in tissue culture using a variety of methods (fig. 13).

Warburg manometry

The conventional Warburg method (Umbreit *et al*, 1948) is suitable when large numbers of cells are available. Cell suspensions are placed in a special flask (fig. 3.1) which contains caustic potash as a carbon dioxide absorbent in the centre well. The flask is attached to a manometer and then immersed in a water bath at 37°C where it is shaken. After allowing the system to equilibrate the manometer is adjusted and closed to the outside atmosphere. Any subsequent drop in pressure is due to oxygen uptake by the cells. This can be measured in a quantitatively reliable way. It has been applied to measure the respiration of HeLa cells (Phillips and McCarthy, 1956) and for Earle's L strain cells (Phillips and Terryberry, 1957).

Leukaemic cells have also been studied by this method (Laszlo *et al*, 1958; Bisset and Alexander, 1960; Woodliff, 1962).

Cartesian diver

Another method of measuring oxygen uptake is by the Cartesian diver technique (fig. 3.2). This is applicable to smaller numbers of cells but is technically much more complex. The cells are placed in a glass diver whose total volume is of the order of 15 microlitres. 0·5 μl of a sodium bicarbonate solution (fig. 3.2c) is added to the bottom of the diver followed by a similar volume of cell suspension to the neck (fig. 3.2d). Further bicarbonate and paraffin oil (fig. 3.2b)

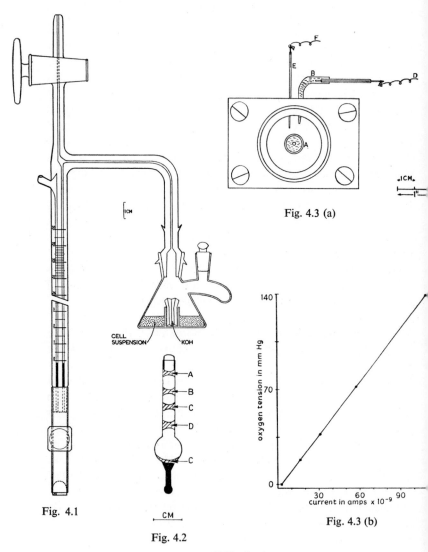

Fig. 4.3 (a)

oxygen tension in mm Hg

140

70

0

30   60   90
current in amps × 10⁻⁹

Fig. 4.3 (b)

Fig. 4.1

CELL
SUSPENSION   KOH

Fig. 4.2

CM

ICM

ICM

F

E

B

A

D

A
B
C
D
C

FIG. 3

METHODS OF MEASURING CELLULAR RESPIRATION
IN VITRO

3.1 Warburg apparatus (see text page 23). 3.2 Cartesian diver (see text page 23).
3.3 Electrochemical method – (a) Chamber and electrode. (b) Relationship
between oxygen tension and current flow (see text page 25).

and water (fig. 3.2a) seals are added. The diver is then immersed at 37°C in a special liquid of known specific gravity. As oxygen is used up, the pressure in the diver becomes reduced. This is compensated for by lowering the pressure in the flotation medium so that the diver remains in one place. This change is read manometrically. The oxygen consumption can then be calculated from a special formula. The method has been used for a variety of cells including blood cells (Kieler, 1957; Bicz, 1960), but the complexities of the apparatus make it unsuitable for general use.

Electrochemical

A third method is to use an electrochemical method of measuring oxygen tension. Although this does not give an absolute figure of oxygen uptake, decreasing oxygen tension indicates that cells are actively respiring. This method of measuring oxygen tension, which was introduced by Daneel in 1897 has been further developed in recent years as a tool in biological research. It is based upon the fact that the current flowing through a fluid from a silver chloride electrode to a precious metal electrode is, under certain defined conditions, proportional to the oxygen tension. There have been some difficulties in developing the technique quantitatively. Davies and Brink (1942) made absolute measurements of oxygen tension but could only make one observation every 5 to 20 minutes; they also found that after one hour the current readings fell gradually when they made *in vitro* measurements. Montgomery and Horwitz (1950) used a similar method to measure oxygen tension in skin, but there was considerable variation in the day to day readings of their electrodes. Cater *et al* (1957) considered that their apparatus could be used to give an approximate measurement of absolute oxygen tension in addition to its useful role of measuring oxygen tension. Cater, Silver and Wilson (1959) developed the technique further and considered that the results were quantitatively reliable; this was further borne out by the work of Davis and Woodliff (1960). Prior to this work the only tissue culture studies in which electrochemical methods of oxygen tension measurements had been employed were those of Harris and Barclay (1955). The apparatus they used to study the respiration of rabbit macrophages differed in detail from the one described here; for example, a potassium chloride agar bridge containing a reference electrode of lead was used. They reported a logarithmic relationship between current flow and oxygen tension, but later Harris (1956), when studying the respiration of the rat connective tissue cells *in vitro* found a curvilinear relationship which he attributed to external resistance of the circuit and to the fact that the potential developed by the lead half cell was not constant but fell with diminishing oxygen tension. In this method (fig. 3.3a) a potential of 600 mV is supplied by a constant output source via lead D to the silver chloride reference electrode B. Oxygen diffusing onto the end of the platinum electrode E is reduced and a current proportional to its tension flows from B through the medium to E which is connected to a sensitive ammeter. The inoculum (A) uses oxygen which diffuses from the medium with a consequent lowering of oxygen tension. The relationship between oxygen tension and current flow, which is linear, is illustrated in fig. 4.3b. From the practical point of view it is important that the relationship between oxygen tension and current flow should be constant.

The electrochemical method of measuring oxygen tension has the advantage of being applicable to small quantities of fluid and therefore can be used to measure indirectly the oxygen uptake of comparatively small numbers of cells. It was applied in this way to study the decrease in oxygen tension in the fluid phase of serum agar culture of normal and leukaemic bone marrow (Woodliff and Davis, 1960). Unfortunately the method has certain technical difficulties which have made constant repetition of this type of experiment difficult and further work is required to perfect the technique.

Carbon dioxide production:

Carbon dioxide is produced by living cells during respiration following oxidation of the carbon in glucose and its products. In tissue cultures carbon dioxide may also be produced by the action of acids (pyruvic and lactic) on bicarbonate ions in the medium. Carbon dioxide production can be measured in the Warburg apparatus. If no carbon dioxide absorbent is present the net volumetric changes, read manometrically, will represent oxygen consumption and carbon dioxide output. If oxygen consumption is measured at the same time the carbon dioxide output can then be calculated. If, in addition, lactic and pyruvic acid measurements are made, the proportion of carbon dioxide due to respiration can be calculated. Such measurements are rather complex but they have been made for HeLa cells and Earle's L cells (Phillips and Feldhaus, 1956 and Philips and McCarthy, 1956). Similar studies of leukaemic cells have been made (Laszlo *et al*, 1958).

The 'net gas output' (carbon dioxide production from both

respiration and acid production less oxygen consumption) of mouse leukaemic cells has also been studied (Woodliff, 1960). Such measurements have the virtue of simplicity and reproducibility, but do not separate the different metabolic changes taking place.

Metabolic quotients:

Various quotients may be worked out from measurements of oxygen, carbon dioxide and acid production studies. These include the respiratory quotient (oxygen consumption divided by respiratory carbon dioxide output) and the ratio of anaerobic to aerobic glycolysis. It has been claimed that from such measurements it is possible to divide cell culture into normal and malignant types. However the differences are only relative and their exact significance is still uncertain.

Other metabolic studies:

Various chemical analyses can be made in cultures both before and after incubation (Osgood and Brownlee, 1937). These include, for example, the decrease in glucose content. Other measurements which detect cell growth rather than cell viability will be discussed later. These include the incorporation of radioactive substances into cells and their detection by autoradiography (Lajtha and Oliver, 1960a) and the uptake of amino acid from the medium (Rinaldini, 1959).

CELL GROWTH

Growth of cultured cells may be assessed by a variety of methods. These include observation and measurement of cell mass, anabolic reactions, increasing cell numbers, deoxyribonucleic acid synthesis, mitotic indices, cell maturation and cell transformation.

Cell mass:

An increase in the mass of cells indicates that growth is taking place; however it does not differentiate between hypertrophy of individual cells and multiplication. In its purest form it involves weighing the cells present both before and during culture. This unfortunately presents considerable technical difficulties. Since it is often difficult to separate the cells from the media, errors may occur. A simple method applicable to plant culture but not, unfortunately, to animal work, is to measure the length of the growing plant roots (White, 1954). The increase in length is proportional to the increase in weight to within ten per cent. The closest approach to this in animal material is to measure the outgrowth of cells from an explant. This however depends not only on measuring cell mass but also on cell motility. Attempts to quantitate such cellular outgrowths have been reported by various authors and some success in this has been achieved for fibroblast-like cells. The method was introduced by Ebeling (1921). It is applicable to solid nutrient substrate cultures in chambers and in small flasks. The image of the outgrowth is usually projected at a fixed magnification onto a screen and the outline of the colony drawn on a piece of squared paper. The area can then be calculated. With some cultures and especially sub-cultures, the increase is fairly regular and reproducible and can therefore be used for quantitative work. Willmer (1933c) perfected a method of automatically photographing the changes in such cultures; unfortunately the apparatus is too complicated for general use. Attempts to measure the outgrowth of cells from serum agar cultures by taking photomicrographs at regular intervals were unsuccessful (Woodliff, 1962). The method was abandoned because of the wide variations which occurred in the controls. The only clearcut differences were between some cellular outgrowth and none; a difference which could be detected by simple microscopic obser-vation.

Other techniques which have been used to assess changes in cell mass include packed cell volume measurements (Gemmill *et al*, 1940) and turbimetric methods (Younger, 1954).

Anabolic reactions:

Actively growing cells synthesise proteins, fats and carbohydrates. These substances can be measured both before and after culture, but errors due to admixture of the medium may occur. Evidence of protein synthesis may also be obtained by measuring the concentration of specific proteins such as haemoglobin (Osgood and Brownlee, 1937) or the uptake amino acids from the medium (Rinaldini, 1959). Other evidence of active anabolism comes from the uptake and incorporation into the cytoplasm of various radioactively labelled precursors (Lajtha, 1960). The radioactivity can be measured either by autoradiography or by measuring the radioactivity of various fractions after chemical extraction. Studies along these lines include the uptake of ^{59}Fe and ^{56}S and the incorporation of compounds labelled with ^{32}P and ^{14}C into cellular constituents.

Haemoglobin synthesis, both in reticulocytes and bone marrow normoblasts, which has been extensively studied by these techniques, cannot be discussed in detail here. The subject is reviewed by

Rimington (1958). Examples of the types of study which have been carried out include those of the incorporation of radioactive amino acids into the protein of rabbit reticulocytes (Borsook *et al*, 1952) and of radioactive iron into human reticulocytes (Walsh *et al*, 1949). Recently the activity of reticulocytes has been utilised in studies of pathological haemoglobin synthesis; for example in the work on thalassaemic blood *in vitro* using ^{14}C – glycine and ^{59}Fe (Bannerman *et al*, 1959).

Studies of radioactive iron uptake by human bone marrow normoblasts *in vitro* (Lajtha and Suit, 1955) have shown that it is similar to that found *in vivo* in rabbit bone marrow (Suit *et al*, 1957). The pronormoblasts and early normoblasts take up most, the intermediate and late normoblasts take up progressively less.

The uptake of radioactive sodium sulphate by cells in marrow cultures was described by Lajtha *et al*, 1953. It was confined to pro-myelocytes, myelocytes and megakaryocytes; lymphocytes and normoblasts did not take up the label. The incorporation of radio-active phosphorus and thymidine into nucleoproteins of cultured bone marrow cells could also be used to study these *in vitro* anabolic reactions.

Cell counts:
The multiplication of cells in culture may be observed by counting the numbers present. Unfortunately, cell counts are subject to many possible errors. The provision of a suspension of single isolated cells either from tissues or from cultures is often difficult, there are always some errors in sampling and counting, and the viability of the counted cells may be in doubt.

Single cell suspensions can be obtained for culture comparatively easily if they are already distributed in a fluid media such as ascites or blood. In the case of solid tissue some process such as enzymic digestion, treatment with chelating agents or mechanical agitation is required. These methods usually damage some of the cells. After counting an aliquot an approximate number of cells are inoculated into replicate culture vessels. Some time later the cells in the cultures are counted. The most exact method is to continuously observe a single cell in culture and to watch it grow into a colony of cells which can be counted directly. This represents a considerable technical feat and has only been achieved for some established cell strains which grow well *in vitro*. More commonly the cells in a sample or in the whole culture are counted. In suspension cultures this can be done by the removal of a sample. In other cultures the cells must be released from the substrate by enzymatic or mechanical means. One of the first attempts to obtain accurate counts of cells in culture utilised a method in which the cell cytoplasm was dissolved and the isolated nuclei counted (Sanford et al, 1950; Evans et al, 1951; Sanford et al, 1952). The counting of whole cells is more often used, but care has to be taken to see that only living cells are included. Various methods have been developed to assess the viability of cells from the cultures. One method is to add a dye which is not taken up by living cells but which stains dead cells and cellular debris. The use of dyes is not completely reliable, since it has been found that non-staining refractile cells with various disturbances of the cytoplasm may be included and their viability is in doubt. Craven (1958) found that HeLa cells of this type were incapable of reproduction. Many workers content themselves by simple inspection of the cells. If under phase contrast illumination they appear to be the correct size and contain a nucleus and normal cytoplasm, they are usually considered to be alive.

Apart from the question of viability the errors of counting in haemocytometer chambers are quite large due to sampling, distribution and subjective factors. At a concentration of about 10×10^6 cells per ml it is unlikely to be less than fifteen per cent, and it may be much more (Biggs, 1951). This must be remembered when assessing the results of cultures based on cell counts.

The problems associated with total cell counts are particularly marked in the case of bone marrow cell cultures. In suspensions of such materials there are usually clumps which make the task of accurate counting difficult. Some authors have attempted to disrupt these clumps by mechanical means such as repeatedly pumping through a needle with a syringe (Lajtha, 1960) or by passing through a stainless steel mesh (Thomas, 1955). Personal experience of these techniques has been disappointing; whilst breaking up of the bigger clumps occurred, aggregates containing many cells remained. Filtration of such suspensions through nylon bolting cloth left too few cells to culture. The viability of some of the cells which have been through such procedures is also doubtful. Attempts to disperse clumps in bone marrow cell suspensions with proteolytic enzymes and chelating agents were also made. Trypsin, chymotrypsin and elastase (Banga and Balo, 1953) were used to treat the cells, as also was the chelating agent ethylenediamine tetracetic acid, both alone and with the proteolytic enzymes. Treatments sufficient to cause complete disaggregation of clumps resulted in cells too damaged to culture. Shorter times which did not damage all the cells failed to disaggregate all the clumps.

Mitoses:

The presence of chromosomes in cells which have been cultured *in vitro* for more than one day indicates that growth is taking place and this in itself can be used as a parameter. In its simplest form the observation that mitotic figures are or are not present may be of some value (Woodliff, 1961). If mitotic counts can be made and are reproducible, the method can be used quantitatively. Counts may be made in the whole culture at different time intervals, or they may be related to the total number of cells present. Whilst regular mitosis indicates an increase in the number of cells, this may be offset by cell death, so that the total number of cells present does not increase. Mitotic counts may therefore be of value in situations where the total cell counts decrease (Woodliff, 1962). They are also of value in cultures where total cell counts are not practical. In cultures in solid nutrient media the central explant is usually too dense for the cells to be counted. However, the cells in the surrounding area can be counted and the proportion of cells in mitoses in these areas calculated. Such mitotic counts are usually made in fixed and stained preparations. However, counts at intervals can be done in living preparations using phase contrast microscopy (Woodliff, 1961). Willmer (1933b) used a method in which photographs were taken of living cells at regular intervals. This allowed the mitotic incidence to be analysed. However, only one culture could be photographed at one time. Whilst mitotic counts of fibroblast-like cells have been developed into reliable quantitative test systems, the irregularity which occurs in bone marrow cell cultures is too great (Woodliff, 1961). Some authors (Jacobson, 1954a and b) have been able not only to estimate the numbers of mitoses, but also to do differential counts as to the different phases – prophase, metaphase, telophase and anaphase. This refinement, possible with fibroblast-like cells, is not applicable to the small numbers found in blood and bone marrow cell cultures. The use of colchicine and related compounds which cause an arrest in metaphase, and thus an accumulation of mitotic figures, often enables a higher mitotic index to be obtained (see p. 88). Such procedures may help in the analysis of cultures in which the multiplication potential of different types of cells is being analysed. They are also helpful in comparing the mitotic rates of the same cell types from different conditions and in studies of cultures treated with agents which might affect cells by preventing or inhibiting mitosis.

Another feature of mitoses which can be measured and is of some interest, is the relative duration of the various phases and of the intermitotic period. This can be measured directly (Woodliff, 1961), or calculated from autoradiographic studies of cultures (Lajtha, 1959).

Deoxyribonucleic acid (DNA) synthesis:

As deoxyribonucleoprotein is found only in the nucleus of cells and is duplicated before each cell division, increased amounts of DNA may be taken as indications of growth and, if appreciable, of nuclear multiplication. The methods available for measuring DNA and the results are reviewed by Waymouth (1951). As far as blood and bone marrow cells are concerned, Gunz (1949) attempted to estimate the DNA concentration in his cultures but did not find the method of value due to the heterogenicity of the cell population and the inaccuracy of the technique employed.

Another approach is to measure the incorporation into DNA of the radioactive elements ^{32}P and ^{14}C (Lajtha *et al*, 1953; Lajtha *et al*, 1954; Brebner *et al*, 1954). This can be demonstrated autoradiographically or by measuring the radioactivity after chemical extraction. Similarly, the uptake of tritiated thymidine is indicative of DNA synthesis.

Spectroscopy of Feulgen stained cells for increasing DNA concentrations between 2n (post mitotic cells) and 4n (cells about to divide) can also be made (Cooper *et al*, 1961); increasing populations of cells with more than 2n indicate DNA synthesis.

Cell maturation:

The terms cell maturation and transformation are used somewhat loosely to describe the changes which may occur in cells both *in vitro* and *in vivo*. It is, however, convenient to distinguish between them. Maturation is used to include those features which are associated with a change from a primitive cell capable of mitosis to a more specialised cell which cannot divide. Examples include the changes from myeloblasts to myelocytes to neutrophil segmented cells, and from pronormoblasts through the early, intermediate and late normoblast stages to the mature erythrocyte. Most of the observations on such changes have been qualitative. An impression was gained by the observer that a certain cell became more frequent in the cultures and another less frequent. The presence of cells intermediate in type strengthened this idea. This type of observation is applicable to many types of culture but lacks accuracy. The best method of deciding definitely the maturation potential of any cell would be to observe it continuously from the end of anaphase until its death. This has been attempted, but it presents considerable technical problems which have not been overcome. However, continuous observation for many hours is possible and a limited amount of information may be gained in this way (Woodliff, 1961).

Other workers have claimed to be able to follow maturation of cells quantitatively, but indirectly, using methods based on total and differential cell counts. The errors in total cell counting have been mentioned above. To this must be added the considerable errors of differential cell counting on smears prepared from cells removed during culture. Thomas (1956) found that unconcentrated smears of bone marrow cell cultures contained too few cells to count, whereas when they were concentrated by centrifugation many necrotic cells were present, as also were clumps of unrecognisable cells. Such smears often have an irregularity in the distribution of the cells and identification of cell type is open to personal bias. When statistical analysis of the results has been made (Sharp *et al*, 1952) the necessity for counting large numbers of cells in many samples has been stressed. It is often difficult to be sure of the identity of cells in smears of bone marrow cell cultures, possibly because of their isolated and relatively rounded state. Some cells are degenerate and although recognisable their prefixation viability is in doubt. This difficulty is less in peripheral blood cell cultures, probably because there are fewer cell types and because they are more easily distinguished from one another. Differential counts from such cultures are practicable (Woodliff, 1962).

Cell transformation:

Cells may transform into cells of another type both *in vivo* and *in vitro*. Such changes seem to occur readily in cell culture. Generally speaking, one of three cell types tends to predominate in long term cultures; these are fibroblast-like cells, epithelial-like cells and macrophage-like cells. These may appear even when similar cells are not found in the original material and the question arises as to the cell or cells of origin. They are often considered to have arisen from other cells by a process of 'transformation'. The only certain method of discovering the transformation potentials of any particular cell is to keep it under continual observation. Many authors, however, have made deductions as to the transformation of cell types from simple inspection of smears from cultures.

In the case of blood and bone marrow cell cultures, all three types described above have been found and in addition a different type of. 'altered' cell has been found in cultures of peripheral blood treated with phytohaemagglutinin. These cells are discussed more fully later (p. 77 and Plate 3).

GENERAL PATTERN OF CULTURE

The features considered in this chapter, such as cellular migration, multiplication and transformation, make up a general pattern which can be recognised for each type of culture. This pattern is of some value in evaluating the cultures, as a departure from it indicates that something is wrong with the cultures or that an added agent is having some effect. It has been used as a crude parameter in both glass substrate and serum agar cultures (Woodliff, 1958, 1961).

CHAPTER 4

Cultures of normal blood and bone marrow cells

The results of culturing normal cells from healthy subjects and from patients with disorders not primarily involving the blood and bone marrow are reviewed in this chapter.

The general pattern of culture is first described and is followed by a more detailed account of the individual cell types. The cultures reviewed here are those in which salt solutions, physiological additives in low concentrations and plasma or serum have been used as media. The effects of adding physiological agents in high concentrations, artificial stimulants and drugs of various kinds are described later.

GENERAL PATTERN OF CULTURE

The general pattern of culture varies with the method used and the nature of the specimen.

In suspension cultures of peripheral blood cells there is a gradual decline in the numbers of cells present with no evidence of cell multiplication.

Bone marrow cell suspension cultures, however, may contain mitotic figures and increasing numbers of nucleated cells (Plum, 1947a and b; Norris and Majnarich, 1948a; Biesele and Berger, 1950). These findings are, however, not constant and when an increase occurs it is not usually large and is limited to a few days. In spite of the multiplication, cell death supervenes and the culture gradually dies. A limited amount of maturation occurs in such cultures (Plum, 1947b).

In glass substrate cultures of adherent peripheral blood cells a decrease in cell numbers is also seen. Cell multiplication does not occur. Persisting cells recognisable as normal blood cells can be found for several days and macrophage type cells may develop in such cultures (Woodliff, 1958a).

D

When bone marrow is cultured by this means three distinct but overlapping cytological phases can be observed. (Berman *et al*, 1956; Woodliff, 1958a). The first phase is that of declining numbers of recognisable marrow and peripheral blood cells, the second that of large granular cells, and the third that of fibroblast-like cells. Berman and his colleagues described a fourth stage in which epithelial-like cells grew in some of the cultures. However, the origin of these cells is not certain. McCulloch and Parker (1956) found that their cultures soon contained large cells, but that later after three to six weeks a sudden change often occurred and a new cell type emerged. Subsequently it was discovered that these cells were contaminating cells of Earle's L strain of mouse fibroblasts. (Rothfels *et al*, 1959). This raises the possibility that the epithelial-like cells in Berman's cultures might also be contaminants, possibly of the HeLa strain. No epithelial or other strains developed in the author's cultures, possibly because no established strains were present in the laboratory as a possible source of contamination.

In *glass substrate deposit cultures* attention has been paid to the loose cells and any adherent cells ignored. Quantitative studies have been more frequently attempted as counts of the resuspended cells can be made. Peripheral blood cells studied by this means decreased in number over five days with no evidence of multiplication or maturation (Thomas, 1956). Bone marrow cell cultures of this type have been made by many authors since their introduction by Osgood and Brownlee in 1936. Osgood (1939a) reported a series of ten normal marrows in which he claimed that multiplication, maturation and functional activities of the granulocyte series of cells were present for up to six weeks. Blackburn and Lajtha (1954) found that in more than 60 per cent of 200 normal bone marrow cultures an absolute increase in the number of polymorphs was found during the twenty-four hours of culture. Smith (1952) reported on the total cell population of normal marrow cultures; he observed an increase of 7 per cent and 19 per cent in two of his three cultures. Thomas, (1956) made the pertinent observation that such increases were unlikely to be significant. In her study Thomas made twenty-four cultures of normal bone marrow, sixteen from ten aspirations of marrow obtained from normal volunteers and eight from four patients suffering from disorders not directly affecting the haemopoietic system. She found great variability in the concentration of cells in different cultures. Some showed slightly increased numbers at first but later the numbers declined. Other cultures had declining numbers from the outset. The average numbers decreased so that at one hundred and twenty hours only about eighty per cent of the cells were present. The random fluctuations were such as to prohibit quantitative assessments. It would seem that this method, whilst giving rise to increased cell numbers for a limited time is not sufficiently constant or reproducible to be reliable for studying normal cells. The fact that mitoses can be found in such cultures has made them valuable for chromosome studies (Ford *et al*, 1958; Sandberg *et al*, 1960). It is also possible to study the incorporation of radioactive substances into the cells and to draw valid conclusions from this type of experiment. Studies on the maturation of cells, based on total and differential cell counts however should also be interpreted with caution. It seems probable that some maturation of cells takes place but attempts to put this on a quantitative basis are subject to many possible errors.

The general pattern of *nutrient solid substrate* cultures is sufficiently similar both in fibrin media and in agar media for them to be considered together. Serum agar cultures have a lesser tendency to be overgrown by fibroblast-like cells, otherwise they resemble plasma clot cultures. In both, motile cells migrate from the inoculum to form a halo around the explant. Peripheral blood cells in such cultures have been studied by several authors (Lewis, 1925; Carrel and Ebeling, 1922, 1926a; and Hirschfeld and Klee-Rawidowicz, 1928). They observed a gradual deterioration of the explanted cells and their alteration and transformation into other cell types. Multiplication of cells does not usually occur and the cultures soon die out. Numerous studies of bone marrow cells cultured in nutrient media have been made since the pioneering days of Carrel and Burrows (1910d) and the Lewises (Lewis and Lewis, 1911a). They include those of Ingerbrigtsen (1912), Meier *et al* (1937a), Rich *et al* (1939), Fieschi and Astaldi (1946a), Albrecht and Boll (1950), Astaldi and Mauri (1950), Baldini and Sacchetti (1953), Sacchetti and Bianchini (1953a and b), Salera and Tamburino (1953), Pulvertaft and Jayne (1953), Pulvertaft and Humble (1956), and Woodliff (1961). Within the limits of the different conditions and methods of observation used there has been good agreement as to the general pattern of culture. Soon after incubation, granulocytes migrate from the explant to form a halo around it. Other motile cells such as monocytes and lymphocytes also migrate out, generally a little later. After a day or so macrophage type cells may be seen. There is a gradual deterioration of the normal haemopoietic cells, usually an increase in macrophage-type cells and finally in some of the cultures an overgrowth of fibroblast-like cells occurs. These may be seen as early as two days and may survive for some considerable time before the culture eventually dies.

CELL TYPES

The cells present in normal blood and bone marrow cell cultures can be divided into three groups, the haemopoietic and mature blood cells, other cells normally found in the bone marrow and altered or transformed cells.

Haemopoietic cells include the haemocytoblast and the granulocytic, monocytic, lymphocytic, plasmacytic, megakaryocyte-thrombocytic and erythrocytic series of cells. Other cells of the bone marrow include reticulum cells, endothelial cells, osteoblasts, osteoclasts, fibroblasts, fat cells and possibly nerve cells.

Altered and transformed cells which cannot be readily classified with the normal cells are large macrophage type cells, fibroblast-like cells and epithelial-like cells.

Haemocytoblasts:

There is still a difference of opinion among haematologists as to whether or not a single recognisable cell is the precursor of all blood cells. The existence of such a cell called the haemocytoblast is a convenient concept and descriptions of it are given in standard text books (Whitby and Britton, 1957). Nevertheless, precise classification of any particular cell as a haemocytoblast remains difficult and, because of this, they are seldom recognised in cell cultures. A few authors have made claims as to their development potentialities *in vitro*. Benevolenskaya (1930) claimed that haemocytoblasts developed into pro-erythroblasts and occasionally into leucocytes in her cultures of human foetal liver. Foot (1912, 1913) in cultures of chicken bone marrow claimed that granulocytes developed from a mesenchymal lymphoid type of cell which could perhaps be classified as a haemocytoblast. In more recent papers haemocytoblasts are not usually mentioned and they have not been recognised in any of the author's cultures. It would be of interest to see if the findings of Benevolenskaya, who used plasma clot cultures observed by sectioning and staining with azur-eosin, could be confirmed with more modern techniques. At present, however, it must be concluded that cell culture techniques have not clarified the position of the haemocytoblast either as to its origin or its potentialities. With advances in technique it is conceivable that identification, separation and culture of such cells might lead to information as to* the factors influencing their multiplication and maturation. More research is necessary in this direction as it may have bearing on the bone marrow cell type which, when inoculated into the circulation following total body irradiation, is capable of proliferation and maturation into functioning haemopoietic tissue.

Granulocytic series:

The *myeloblast* is generally accepted as being the most primitive cell of the granulocytic series and it is thought to give rise by maturation through promyelocyte, myelocyte and metamyelocyte stages to mature neutrophil, eosinophil and basophil leucocytes. This theory of maturation is based on microscopical studies of cells intermediate between the various types. Myeloblasts are only infrequently mentioned in the literature on normal bone marrow cell cultures. Benevolenskaya (1930) described them in cultures of normal human embryonic liver and found that maturation along the accepted lines was occurring. Rassmussen (1933) found that myeloblasts from the bone marrow of young rabbits cultured in plasma clots, divided for some days and occasionally turned into myelocytes. Smith (1952) found such cells in the inocula of his fluid deposit cultures and that they declined in numbers until none were present at 140 hours. Thomas (1956) who classified myeloblasts and promyelocytes together as primitive granulocytic cells, found that there was a slight increase in these cells at six hours, followed by a steady decline to 120 hours in her glass substrate deposit cultures. The present author has not been able to identify these cells with certainty in any of his cultures. The evidence available suggests that normal myeloblasts multiply and have a maturation potential *in vitro* similar to that *in vivo*. Because of the difficulties in technique however, this cannot yet be accepted as proved. The isolation and separation of such cells followed by close observation of their *in vitro* behaviour would provide more direct evidence as to their potentialities and such studies are required before the question can be finally settled.

The *promyelocyte* is an intermediate stage between the myeloblast and the myelocyte. It is not usually recorded separately in the accounts of bone marrow cell cultures. However Smith (1952) reported that increased numbers of promyelocytes in the first six hours of culture were followed by a fall at 140 hours. This could be interpreted as multiplication followed by maturation. Such cells have occasionally been observed by the author in serum agar cultures; no motility, division or maturation was seen. The differences in behaviour may be due to the different techniques used and it is not as yet possible to be certain as to the *in vitro* behaviour of promyelocytes.

Neutrophil myelocytes are readily recognised in cultures; it is generally accepted that they are derived from promyelocytes, are capable of mitosis and produce neutrophil metamylocytes by naturation. mitotable and produce neutrophil metamyelocytes by maturation.

They are described as being non-motile by some (Ackerman and Bellios, 1955a and b; Pulvertaft and Humble, 1956), but the present author has occasionally seen them migrate, usually after division (Woodliff, 1961). Rassmussen (1933) claimed that they were derived from myeloblasts in her cultures of young rabbit bone marrow. Other authors (Grossman, 1924; and Spadafina, 1935) made the point that myelocytes outlived the more mature granulocytes in their cell culture of guinea pig and rabbit bone marrow. In her glass substrate fluid deposit cultures of normal bone marrow, Thomas (1956) found a slight increase of these cells at six hours followed by a steady fall to 120 hours. There was great variability. Mitotic figures (Plate 2) have been seen in cells of this type in most types of cultures (Lajtha, 1952; Thomas, 1956; Pulvertaft and Humble, 1956; Woodliff, 1961). In the author's serum agar preparations the greatest number counted in any one fleck was 26, but a more usual number was 3 or 4. Prophase could be recognised only occasionally; the cells were usually in metaphase when first seen. The timing of the metaphase varied widely from 15 minutes to 3 hours before anaphase commenced. Some cells were arrested in metaphase and degenerated before completing mitosis. This and the variable timing may have been due to the light used during observation, as it was noted that cells frequently examined generally took longer to divide than those examined occasionally. Once anaphase commenced it was usually completed in a few minutes and telophase took from 10 to 30 minutes before complete reconstitution of the nuclei. During metaphase cells were seen to rotate in both a clockwise and anticlockwise direction and cytoplasmic bubbling was frequent.

Usually the two daughter cells were similar but on one occasion one daughter cell had a reniform nucleus whilst the other was oval

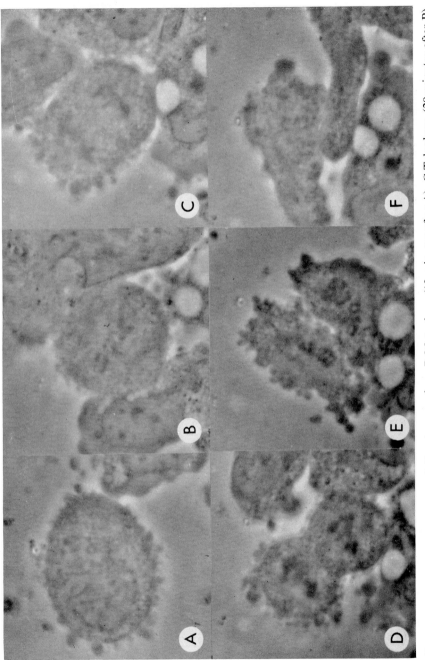

5a MITOSES OF A MYELOCYTES: A Prophase nucleus. B Metaphase (12 minutes after A). C Telophase (29 minutes after B). D Telophase (1 minute after C). E Anaphase (5 minutes after D). F Daughter cells (8 minutes after E)

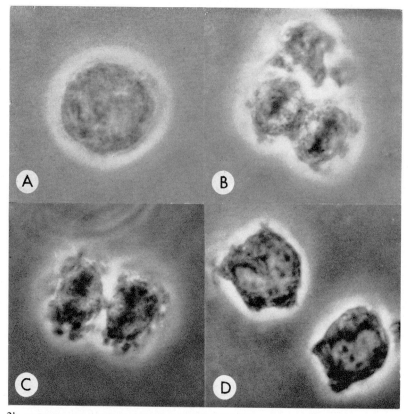

2b MITOSIS OF A MYELOCYTE GIVING RISE TO A DAUGHTER CELL WITH A
KIDNEY-SHAPED NUCLEUS: A Metaphase. B Telophase (45 minutes after A).
C Telophase (7 minutes after B). D Daughter cells (170 minutes after C.)

(Plate 2). This is the only evidence of maturation seen in cells in the author's culture. Pulvertaft and Humble (1956) found that these cells did not mature. This lack of maturation may be peculiar to the type of culture as there is evidence that maturation may take place in fluid deposit cultures.

Usually only one division of the myelocyte has been seen in serum agar cultures. However, on one occasion, the author followed the daughter cells into a further division. The interphase was 10 hours and 15 minutes for one daughter cell and 11 hours and 10 minutes for the other. Lajtha (1957) using autoradiographic studies of cells in deposit cultures found that myelocytes had a multiplication cycle lasting about 48 hours.

The secretion of small vacuoles by myelocytes has been reported and illustrated by Richter (1955). The author has confirmed this observation in serum agar cultures. Small vacuoles were extruded from small myelocytes, usually soon after division.

Although there is ample evidence that mitoses of normal myelocytes takes place *in vitro*, their frequency may be so irregular as to make quantitative studies unreliable. So far no information has been obtained as to the control of this process.

Maturation also takes place in some types of culture but not in all. Studies with ^{32}s sodium sulphate suggested that myelocytes in fluid deposit cultures matured to segmented forms in about 24 hours (Lajtha *et al*, 1953).

Neutrophil metamyelocytes are derived from myelocytes by a process of maturation. They do not divide and they mature into segmented neutrophils. Thomas (1956) found that the numbers of these cells generally decreased in her cultures over 24 hours; however, there was great variability and in some of her cultures the numbers increased. These findings are compatible with some maturation. Pulvertaft and Humble (1956) found that these cells were sluggishly motile in serum agar preparations and this has been confirmed by the author. Maturation into segmented cells has not been found in preparations of this type.

Division of these cells does not occur and although their formation by maturation from myelocytes and development into segmented neutrophils may occur in some types of culture this is by no means invariable.

Neutrophil segmented granulocytes are present in normal blood and are derived from metamyelocytes. Some authors define an intermediate non-segmented granulocyte found in the peripheral blood called a band cell. With progressive age the cells are thought to become more highly segmented. These cells have frequently been observed in cultures of peripheral blood and were recognised as long ago as 1865 by Schultz. Lewis (1925) observed them in chicken, rabbit and human blood cultures; they degenerated and disappeared during the first week. Their motility *in vitro* has been frequently described (Lewis, 1927); they do not divide.

Healthy motile cells of this series can be found for several days in many types of culture (Osgood, 1937; Thomas, 1956; Woodliff, 1958, 1961). Many, however, show degenerative changes in the cytoplasm and homogenisation of the nuclear material. Quantitative studies have been made by some authors. Osgood found such cells in his culture up to seven days, but the majority lived for 48 to 90 hours with an average of 61 hours. The number of mature neutrophils increased in the early stage of the cultures. Thomas (1956) found a wide variation, but on the average a decrease at 6 hours followed by a slight rise to pre-existing levels at 72 hours, followed by a drop at 120 hours.

Where increased numbers of these cells are found it seems likely that maturation from metamyelocytes is occurring.

Eosinophil myelocytes are readily recognised in culture; they are derived from promyelocytes and are the first recognisable cells of the eosinophil series. They mature into segmented eosinophil leucocytes. They have not been extensively studied in culture. Osgood (1937) found that eosinophil precursors were frequently seen in division in his cultures, but that more mature cells did not divide. From this and other observations he concluded that eosinophils lived for eight to twelve days *in vitro*. Pulvertaft and Humble (1956) did not see any evidence of division of eosinophil myelocytes in their serum agar culture. The author has not observed a complete cell division; however, on one occasion, an eosinophil myelocyte was seen to mitose. The two daughter nuclei recombined to form a single nucleus and there was no cytokinesis.

Eosinophil segmented granulocytes survive in many types of cultures for many days. They appear to be more hardy than neutrophils in this respect.

Basophil myelocytes and tissue mast cells have rarely been recognised in cell cultures. Osgood (1937) describes their presence and concluded that cells of this series have a life span of twelve to fifteen days. The author has observed *segmented basophil granulocytes* surviving in peripheral blood cell cultures at four days.

Monocytic series:

Monocytes are generally thought to arise from cells of the reticular system in the bone marrow, lymph node, spleen and other tissues. Whether they mature through haemocytoblast and monoblast stages is not known and culture studies have not contributed to this problem. *Monocyte precursors* are not commonly recognised in blood and bone marrow cell cultures. Van den Berghe *et al* (1938), however, describe the development of mature moncytes from promonocytes in cultures of ape's bone marrow. The *mature monocyte* can be recognised in most types of culture for several days. The main cell culture interest in monocytes has been in their developmental potentialities. Frequently they have been thought to give rise to the common macrophage type cell found in many cultures. However, there are no reports of experiments where this actual transformation has been followed in the living cell. It is also frequently stated that they may develop into fibroblast-like cells (Avroroff and Timofeevsky 1915, quoted by Bloom 1938; Carrel and Ebeling, 1922, 1926a; Fischer, 1925; and Haagen, 1927). The present author has observed human monocytes in culture but could not say whether or not they transformed into other cell types. The fact that fibroblast-like cells developed in cultures of bone marrow but not of peripheral blood (Woodliff, 1958) does not support the view that monocytes can transform into fibroblast-like cells. Apart from confirming the well-known phagocytic properties of these cells, culture studies have been unrewarding.

Lymphocytic series:

Lymphocytes arise by maturation of lymphoblasts which in their turn are thought to arise from maturation of haemocytoblasts in the lymphoid tissues.

Lymphoblasts are not usually recognised in bone marrow cell cultures. *Lymphocytes* are present in both blood and bone marrow cell cultures where they may survive for many days. They are actively motile progressing with the nucleus in front and a train of cytoplasm behind; this is often called the 'hand mirror' form. Cell culture studies have not contributed to the origin of the lymphocytes. Most accounts of culture studies of lymphocytes are concerned with their developmental potentialities. According to Bloom (1938), Avroroff and Timofeevsky (1915) in their cultures of leucocytes from the normal rabbit, dog and guinea pig observed the transformation of lymphocytes into macrophage-type and fibroblast-like cells. Maximow (1927) also studied the potentialities of the lymphocyte in various species; he considered that he had demonstrated the transformation of the small lymphocyte into a macrophage (polyblast) and further into a fibroblast. Using cultures of guinea pig blood observed by sectioning and by supravital staining, he was able to state 'This direct observation proves beyond doubt the rapid development of the lymphocytes into polyblasts (macrophages)'. This concept cannot be accepted without question; his starting material was a mixed cell population and it is possible that the macrophages developed from monocytes. Certain proof can only come from the direct observation of a single lymphocyte into such an altered cell. However, there is much support in the early literature for Maximow's views (Timofeevsky and Benevolenskaya, 1926; Bloom, 1927; Caffierm 1927, 1928; de Haan, 1928; Lacassagne and Gricouroff, 1927; Vasiliu and Stoica, 1929; and Bisceglie, 1929). Maximow (1932) later stated that lymphocytes could also give rise to plasma cells.

Wetheman (1932) and Reeves (1934) found no evidence of lymphocytic transformation and this view is supported by later workers. Lymphocytes in cultures observed by the author have degenerated and died after periods varying from a few hours to several days without evidence of transformation.

Pulvertaft et al (Humble, Jayne and Pulvertaft, 1956; Pulvertaft, 1959) have made a special study of the behaviour of lymphocytes in serum agar cultures of bone marrow. Most of the material studied was pathological but they infer that cells from normal human marrow were also studied. They found a relationship between lymphocytes and malignant cells, cells in mitosis and megakaryocytes in which the lymphocytes became adherent to the other cells and apparently passed over or into them. The term emperipolesis was used to describe this phenomenon. I have observed lymphocytes approaching a large cell, probably a megakaryocyte, and travelling around it in a serum agar preparation of normal bone marrow. In an attempt to see whether the circulation of lymphocytes around such cells was due to the physical or biological properties of the large cells, a number of cultures of lymphocytes mixed with small glass beads was made. Lymphocytes sometimes approached the beads and circulated round them.

Plasmocytic series:

The origin of plasmocytes is uncertain; some believe that they arise directly from reticulum cells, others that they mature from haemocytoblasts through a plasmoblast stage. Others believe they are derived from lymphocytes (Maximow, 1932).

Plasmocytes and their precursors may be found in bone marrow and occasionally in peripheral blood but they are not often recognised in cell cultures. *In vitro* studies have not contributed to our understanding of the origin and developmental potentialities of the cells. However, studies of single isolated cells have shown them to be capable of *in vitro* synthesis of antibodies (Nossal, 1962).

Megakaryocyte-thrombocytic series:

The megakaryocytes are thought to be derived from the haemocytoblast through a megakaryoblast stage. They give rise to thrombocytes (Wright, 1906).

Studies of megakaryocytes in bone marrow cell cultures have been disappointing until recently and there are few references to them in the older literature. Rassmussen (1933) culturing marrow from young rabbits claimed that new megakaryocytes arise from large lymphoid cells and that they had amoeboid motions and were phagocytic. There was no evidence of platelet formation in these cultures nor in Spadafina's (1935).

In recent years several authors have seen actual platelet formation taking place *in vitro* in cultures. Thiery and Bessis (1956a and b), Pulvertaft (Pulvertaft and Humble, 1956; and Pulvertaft, 1958), Albrecht (1957), Izak *et al* (1957) and Hiraki (1958) have all contributed to this subject.

Thiery and Bessis mention that it had previously been noted that in human material megakaryocytes commence to degenerate when studied by phase contrast. They therefore modified the technique using material taken from rats and mice immediately after death. Examination at 37°C showed many cells in a state of thrombocytogenesis. They show a photograph of a megakaryocyte at the beginning of observation and the same cell after 5 hours. The nucleus remains as before and the cytoplasm has been altered into many long strands containing swellings which they claimed were the platelets.

Pulvertaft and Humble found that on one occasion they observed the first stages of platelet formation as described by Thiery and Bessis. The photograph illustrating this shows several cytoplasmic projections, some of which are beaded. Later Pulvertaft (1958) found that low oxygen tension stimulated thrombocytogenesis and presented photographic stills of the process taken from a time lapse ciné film. I have observed a megakaryocyte in a serum agar culture of bone marrow for several hours after fluid in the well of the culture had been bubbled with nitrogen gas in an attempt to displace the oxygen present. It produced cytoplasmic extensions similar to those illustrated by other authors. However, no separation of the extended cytoplasm to form platelets was seen. Several other megakaryocytes were subsequently studied under a variety of conditions. Although many cytoplasmic contortions took place no active platelet formation was seen. Albrecht published photographs of similar cytoplasmic prolongations of megakaryocytes. These were observed in tissue cultures of human bone marrow with the aid of cinematography. She discussed several methods of platelet production. The megakaryocytes showed lively amoeboid cytoplasmic movements and in some cases the whole megakaryocyte dissolved into platelets, whereas in others individual platelets were given off. Platelets produced in the culture were often connected with each other in the form of chains; this, she thought, might be due to the high content of substances enhancing clotting in the medium. Whilst the photographs in her paper show elongated strings of cytoplasm, which could be groups of platelets strung together, there is no clear picture of the actual production of single platelets. Hiraki has claimed that he was the first to succeed in detecting active movement of megakaryocytes; pursuing his research he made further observations on normal megakaryocytes, some of which migrated from the marrow flecks with pseudopodial movements, Many had bizarre shapes and in the mature megakaryocyte tentacle-like processes were observed in addition to pseudopodia. The tips of these tentacles grew larger and a constriction occurred between them and the remaining part of the tentacles. The tip sometimes separated from the tentacle into the surrounding medium, thus making a platelet. The photographs which accompany this paper show these cytoplasmic projections, but again there is no convincing evidence in the still photographs of actual platelet production. From his observations he puts forward the hypothesis that the megakaryocyte, matured in the interstitial tissue of the bone marrow, migrates to the wall of the sinusoids and throws out tentacles which press through the wall and send platelets into the circulation.

Although these authors appear to have seen platelet production, the photographs published so far are not convincing. It seems likely however that it is taking place and it might be possible to study thrombopoietic factors by similar *in vitro* techniques.

Erythrocytic series:

Erythrocytes are derived from haemocytoblasts by a process of multiplication and maturation which includes the following intermediate stages – pronormoblast, early, intermediate and late normoblasts and proerythrocytes.

Studies of normoblasts in tissue culture have been concerned with their origin, multiplication and maturation. One of the first studies was by Van Herwerden (1918) who observed living cultures of rabbit, guinea pig and cat bone marrow and saw expulsion of the nuclei of erythroblasts, a finding also reported by Grossman (1924), Rassmussen (1933) and Albrecht (1951) in rabbits and guinea pigs. Mas y Magro (1932) describes the appearance of erythrocytic cells in his cultures of marrow from mammals and birds. He considered that they were derived from endothelium and describes progressive haemoglobinisation of the normoblasts. Spadafina (1935) reported the development of erythroblasts into erythrocytes with probable extrusion of the nucleus, in cultures of guinea pig and rabbit bone marrows. Rachmilewitz and Rosin (1943) who studied human bone marrow in plasma clot cultures regarded it as highly probable that maturation of erythroid cells was taking place in their culture. Lajtha (1952) studied 23 normal marrows in deposit cultures and found limited multiplication which did not keep step with differentiation resulting in a gradual accumulation of the late cell forms. Pulvertaft and Humble (1956) found that mitosis occurred frequently amongst normoblasts in their serum agar cultures. The cells however did not survive long and often lysed in the final stages of mitosis. They found that those that completed the cycle gave rise to two identical daughter cells. They also saw the extrusion of the nucleus of late normoblasts. Mitotic figures were frequently observed in normoblasts in the author's serum agar preparations but complete karyokinesis was never seen, nor was extrusion of the nucleus. The cells remained morphologically intact for up to 48 hours, after which they degenerated (Woodliff, 1961).

Lajtha (1957), using autoradiographic studies of cells in fluid deposit culture, found that early normoblasts had a cycle time of about 24 hours. From these and other studies he has put forward a model of the erythron in which 20 mature erythrocytes are seen to develop from one stem cell (Lajtha and Oliver, 1959). It may be concluded that whilst multiplication and maturation of erythrocytic cells has been shown to take place in some types of cell culture, special techniques are needed to quantitate this in a reliable way.

Other normal bone marrow cells:

As well as the haemopoietic and blood cells the bone marrow contains osteoclasts, osteoblasts, fat cells, fibroblasts, reticulum cells, endothelial cells and possibly nerve cells. Cells of these types are not often seen in bone marrow cultures and there is little information regarding their behaviour *in vitro*. Foot (1912) described the development of fat cells from non-fat containing precursors. However, it is possible that these and the fat cells which developed in Erdmann's (1917a and b) cultures represented cell transformation rather than the true development of fat cells. Phagocytic reticulum cells are occasionally seen in culture but do not appear to divide or mature.

Transformed and altered cells:

Transformed and altered cells have been frequently described in cultures of blood and bone marrow cells. Generally speaking, they correspond to the three classical cell culture types, the macrophage-type cell, the fibroblast-like cell and the epithelial-like cell.

Macrophage-type cells

A wide variety of names such as histiocyte, polyblast, large granular cell and clasmocyte have been given to cells of this type. It is quite possible that several different types of cells are included under this overall heading and that cells of this type have a multiple origin. The cells vary in morphology; generally speaking, they are large with a big nucleus and abundant cytoplasm. The nucleus is homogenous except for one or two nucleoli which may be present. The cytoplasm may contain a variety of inclusions such as granules and vacuoles as well as mitochondria. The cells may be rounded or elongated. They adhere to glass and show sluggish amoeboid activity. It has been suggested that these cells are derived from monocytes and that they may develop into fibroblast-like cells. Some claim that they divide mitotically but rapid multiplication is certainly not a feature of this cell and it is difficult to subculture it *in vitro*.

Avroroff and Timofeevsky (1915, quoted by Bloom, 1938) found such cells (polyblasts) in their cultures of normal leucocytes.

Carrel and Ebeling (1922) obtained a pure culture of mononuclear leucocytes from adult chicks which they kept alive for three months;

these were probably cells which would not be regarded as the macrophage-type. Some of the cells changed into fibroblast-like cells, especially if Rous virus was added (Carrel and Ebeling, 1926a).

Fischer (1925) found that macrophages were transformed into fibroblast-like cells if dead muscle was added to the cultures. Lewis (1925 and 1926) found large macrophages in her cultures which she believed were derived from monocytes. Four or five days later they became larger and turned into epithelioid cells. Binuclear and multinucleated cells of the Langerhan's type were also seen.

Maximow (1927) made an extensive study of these cells, which he considered were derived from lymphocytes and monocytes and could themselves turn into fibroblast-like cells. Timofeevsky and Benevolenskaya (1926) also found that lymphocytes and monocytes from the buffy coat of chickens and rabbit blood turned into macrophages when cultured; similar results were reported by Caffier (1927, 1928), Lacassagne and Gricouroff (1927), Vasiliu and Stoica (1929), Bisceglie (1929) and Katzenstein (1931). The development of these cells in cultures of normal peripheral blood has been noted but their origin could not be determined (Woodliff, 1958a). Macrophage-type cells changed into fibroblast-like cells, epithelioid and giant cells in cultures described by Weiss and Fawcett (1953), who studied material from chickens. Such changes have not been seen in human material.

Fibroblast-like cells

These cells resemble fibroblasts seen in sections of fibrous tissue. Since the actual development of fibres is not usually seen in cultures containing these cells, the term fibroblast-like cells is preferred. The cells are large and elongated, the nucleus is large and usually contains one or two, and occasionally up to twelve, nucleoli. The cytoplasm may contain a number of inclusions, but is often clear except for the mitochondria which are clearly seen in phase contrast preparations (Plate 1). The cells migrate by means of a gliding motion and they multiply by quite frequent mitosis (Plate 1). motion and they multiply by quite frequent mitosis (fig. 3).

These cells have been found in peripheral blood cultures by a number of authors who consider they develop from macrophages or directly from monocytes or lymphocytes (Avrowoff and Timofeevsky, 1915; Carrel and Ebeling, 1922 and 1926a; Fischer, 1925; Maximow, 1927; Haagen, 1926; Caffier, 1927 and 1928; De Haan, 1928; Vasiliu and Stoica, 1929; Bisceglie, 1929; and Katzenstein, 1931). Maximow (1928 and 1929) actually reported the development of reticular and collagen fibres in cultures of blood leucocytes of a guinea pig after 25 days. The author has not seen fibroblast-like cells developing in cultures of peripheral blood. Fibroblast-like cells have been found in practically all types of bone marrow cell cultures made on solid media. The main point of interest is their origin. If it is accepted that such cells can develop from peripheral blood, they probably originate from monocytes or lymphocytes. However fibroblast-like cells are more frequently found in bone marrow cell cultures and other possible sources such as reticular cells, tissue fibroblasts and myelocytes must be considered. So far all the evidence as to their origin is indirect and the final answer must await a technique which allows the continuous observation of the potentialities of a single cell.

Since the presence of these cells may interfere with the observation of other cells, several methods have been used in an attempt to suppress their development. Shaffer (1956) treated his explants with a lecithinase, and Rose et al (1958) developed a cellophane strip technique in which fibroblast-like cell formation was inhibited. Recently it has been reported that collagenase inhibits fibroblasts in bone marrow cultures (Farnes and Trobaugh, 1961a).

Reisner (Reisner, 1959; Edward, Reisner and Odom, 1959) reported that they could be prevented from appearing by using a deep well culture. He placed large (5 mm) explants of marrow from ribs resected by surgical operation in the bottom of a small glass well made from a 10×18 mm glass cylinder ring on a coverslip. The explant was prevented from floating by placing a circle of tantalum gauze mesh over it. If a shallow layer of fluid was added to the culture then fibroblasts grew out of the explant. However, if the well contained a deep layer of fluid, fibroblasts did not develop and maturing cells migrated out of the explant for several months. He considered that the fibroblasts might represent haemocytoblasts and that according to the conditions of culture they multiplied without maturation or matured without multiplication. Farnes and Trobaugh (1961b) were unable to confirm this finding; using the same technique they found fibroblasts even in deep well culture.

Puck et al (1957) studied the nutritional requirements of fibroblast-like and epithelial-like cells from a variety of human tissues including bone marrow. They found fibroblast-like cells to be more demanding, initially requiring embryo extract, for optimal growth. By the use of differential media they could grow either fibroblast-like or epithelial-like cells from dispersed single cells obtained by trypsinisation of human embryonic lung. They do not appear to have used this procedure for bone marrow.

Whilst fibroblast-like cells are of general cytological interest and can readily be obtained from bone marrow, their significance in regard to haemopoiesis is at present obscure.

Epithelial-like cells

Occasionally an epithelial-like type of cell resembling the classical tissue culture strains such as HeLa has been found in cultures of blood and bone marrow cells. Berman *et al* (1955) reported a strain of such cells which they found in a bone marrow culture. Since the patient had a carcinoma of the lung the possibility that it was derived from a malignant cell was entertained. Subsequently, however, five more strains derived from bone marrow were reported (Berman and Stulberg, 1956; Berman *et al*, 1957a and b), and two of these patients had no malignant disease; one had diabetes mellitus and the other a refractive error. The possibility that these cells are contaminants has been discussed previously (page 36). Even if they are in fact transformed blood or bone marrow cells, it is difficult to see their significance in haemopoiesis.

E

CHAPTER 5

Cultures of abnormal blood and bone marrow cells

In this chapter the results of culturing cells from patients with disorders of haemopoiesis are reviewed. The disorders are classified according to the cell series mainly involved; however, it must be remembered that in some instances several cell types are affected.

Haemocytoblasts:

Disorders of these cells can be divided into hypoplastic, aplastic and neoplastic states. Diminution of the numbers or absence of haemocytoblasts may be responsible for some of the disorders characterised by pancytopenia; however, our knowledge of such conditions is meagre and cell cultures have not contributed to our understanding of the problem. Neoplastic change of haemocytoblasts may give rise to some forms of acute leukaemia. Difficulties in classification arise here, for whilst one observer may call cells from a patient with an acute leukaemia 'haemocytoblasts or stem cells', others might call them myeloblasts, monoblasts or lymphoblasts. For these reasons, all acute leukaemia cells are considered together in the next section.

Acute leukaemia cells:

The predominant leucocyte found in the blood and bone marrow of patients with acute leukaemia is generally referred to as a 'blast' cell. Such cells, which are capable of division, have relatively large nuclei with a fine chromatin pattern and often one or more nucleoli. The cytoplasm is usually relatively scanty and deeply basophilic when stained panoptically (Hayhoe, 1960). Whilst the cells from any one case may be uniform, considerable pleomorphism occurs in the group as a whole. This makes classification on conventional lines difficult; however, it is usual to divide them into myeloblastic, lymphoblastic or monoblastic cell types. Where this is not possible, the cells are referred to as haemocytoblasts or stem cells. Studies of these cells in culture have been made by numerous authors and have generally been directed towards comparing the leukaemic cells with normal cells by studying their viability, motility, metabolism, multiplication, maturation and transformation as well as their general pattern of culture. Cultures have also been used as a help in classifying the cells.

Cell survival

Acute leukaemic cells in tissue culture usually die within a few days although those from cases of monocytic leukaemia may survive for several weeks (Israels, 1940b). A few established cell strains have been isolated from leukaemic blood, and they are discussed more fully later. Comparisons between surviving leukaemic cells and normal haemopoietic cells are difficult, as blast cells are found only in small numbers in normal material. However there is probably little difference between the *in vitro* survival of luekaemic and normal cells.

Motility

Studies of the motility of acute leukaemic cells have been made by several authors. Rich *et al* (1939) cultured leukaemic myeloblasts and noted that their motility was different from that of the leukaemic lymphoblast. They studied six cases of myeloid leukaemia and found that the myeloblasts resembled those found in normal rabbit marrow in that they had a worm-like locomotion. Lymphoblasts from ten cases migrated out with a steady movement with persistent anterior and posterior ends and a rather fixed shape. They suggested that the two cell types could be differentiated by this means. De Bruyn (1944) however demonstrated that these differences in locomotion were due to physical factors in the cultures rather than the nature of the cells. The cells from five lymphoblastic and one myeloblastic leukaemias studied by the author showed no differences in their motility. All had rather sluggish movements of the lymphoid type; that is, an amoeboid movement with the nucleus to the front and a tail of cytoplasm behind, the so-called 'hand mirror' form. Pulvertaft and Humble (1960), however, could differentiate the two types; the lymphoblasts had the positive movement pattern and cytoplasmic organelle arrangement found in lymphocytes, and the myeloblasts had a sluggish and hesitant motility with a marked tendency to develop fine cytoplasmic granulation after twenty-four hours of culture.

Cells from monocytic leukaemia can more readily be differentiated because of their active motility, their extensive pseudopodial formation and their phagocytic activity. Pulvertaft and Humble (1960) also describe a darting and swooping movement of these cells. They found that the presence of peroxidase negative monocytes was associated with a poor prognosis. They were found in cases of pure monocytic (Schilling) leukaemia. In a second type of monocytic leukaemia cells were less motile, had short, broad pseudopodia, and were less phagocytic. Such cells were feebly peroxidase positive and were associated with a better prognosis. They were found in cases of myelomonocytic (Naegeli) leukaemia (Humble, 1962).

Differences in motility also affect the general pattern of the culture; this is considered below.

Metabolism

The oxygen uptake of leukaemic cells has been studied by means of the Cartesian Diver technique by Kieler (1957) and by Bicz (1960). Substantial differences between normal and leukaemic cells were found by Kieler, who reported figures of 0·50, 0·37 and 0·50 μμl per cell per hour for acute leukaemic cells and 6·74 μμl per cell per hour for normal cells. Bicz, however, did not find such large differences as Kieler. The results with leukaemic cells were similar, but those for normal cells averaged 0·26 μμl/cell/hour. Kieler (1959) was inclined to believe that Bicz's figures for normal cells rather than his own were correct.

Similar studies, but using a Warburg apparatus and including some other aspects of energy metabolism of acute leukaemia cells have been made (Laszlo *et al*, 1958; Woodliff, 1962). Laszlo and his colleagues measured aerobic glycolysis, oxygen uptake and carbon dioxide production of cells from eight patients with acute lymphoblastic leukaemia and five with acute myeloblastic leukaemia. The results of two cases, one of each type, are given in detail. The lymphoblasts had a low respiratory quotient (0·27) and a high ratio of aerobic glycolysis to respiration, which the authors say is typical of cancer tissue. The myeloblasts had a higher respiratory quotient (0·71) which was in the normal range, and a high aerobic glycolysis typical of a malignant metabolism. Although they gave no figures, the authors state that the aerobic glycolysis of normal human intact leucocytes was also high and indistinguishable from those of acute myelogenous leukaemia. Their results of oxygen uptake were given in microlitres per mgm of dry weight of cells per hour, and they also

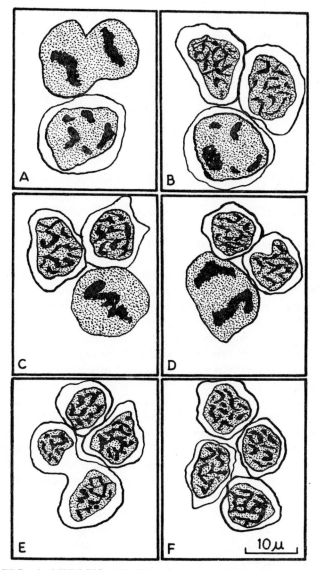

FIG. 4. MITOSIS OF CELLS FROM THE MARROW
OF A PATIENT WITH ACUTE LEUKAEMIA
(Drawings from original photographs)

(A) Four hour culture of two cells, one in telophase. (B) The same field 13 minutes
after (A); the nuclei of the daughter cells are reconstituting. (C) The same field
53 minutes after (A); the other cell is now in mitosis (metaphase). (D) The same
field 75 minutes after (A); anaphase. (E) The same field 84 minutes after (A);
commencing cytokinesis. (F) The same field 120 minutes after (A); the four
daughter cells.

stated that 1 mgm of dry weight was equivalent to fourteen million cells. The oxygen consumption of the lymphoblasts was 4·8 µl/mg/hour; recalculated on the basis of the above figures this is 0·34 µµl/cell/hour. The oxygen consumption of the myeloblasts was 5·6 µl/mg/hour; this is equivalent to 0·4 µµl/cell/hour. These figures are of the same order as those obtained by the author (0·25 – 0·3 µµl for cells obtained from four cases of human acute leukaemia).

Multiplication

The presence of mitoses in leukaemic blast cells has been noted by many writers (fig. 4). However, cell multiplication is usually more than offset by cell lysis. With the exception of the cell strains isolated by Osgood and the strains of mouse leukaemic cells described below leukaemic cells die out within a few days or weeks. Quantitative evidence on the *in vitro* multiplication of human acute leukaemia cells has been presented by Fieschi *et al* (1956). These authors measured mitotic indices following treatment of the cultures with colchicine. The indices per thousand for the types of cells they recognised were – microhaemocytoblasts 10·6, lymphoblasts 8 to 15, unclassifiable blast cells 15 to 22, monoblasts and promyelocytes 46. The index for promyelocytes of normal bone marrow averaged 78.5. From this research they concluded that the multiplication time of acute leukaemic cells is greater than that of normal granuloblasts. These results are complimented by the work of others (Lajtha *et al*, 1954; Gavosto *et al*, 1960; Craddock and Nakai, 1962) who have found that the blast cells from acute leukaemias have a markedly slower rate of DNA synthesis than normal promyelocytes and myelocytes. They are of interest because it is generally thought that malignant cells have a shorter generation time than normal. The relative times of interphase and mitosis have not been well documented, but observation of a few mitoses in acute leukaemic cells suggests that mitosis itself takes about the same time as in normal myelocytes. This is in agreement with the results of the DNA synthesis study which suggested that it was the interphase rather than mitosis which was prolonged in leukaemic blast cells.

Even when multiplication is found in these cells it occurs for only a few generations and is usually more than offset by cellular lysis. Established cell strains and some long term cultures have however been reported. The only claims to success with human material are those of Osgood and Brooke (Osgood and Brooke, 1955; Brooke and Osgood, 1959). They have isolated several cell strains from the blood and bone marrow of patients with acute leukaemia. The first strains (J 96 and J 111) were obtained from the blood of patients with monoblastic leukaemias. The cells of these strains show considerable pleomorphism and they do not resemble leukaemic monoblasts morphologically. Subsequent cell strains have been isolated by adding blood or bone marrow to established cultures of J 111 cells which act as feeder cells. Although the newer strains at first retained some morphological similarities with the inoculum, they soon developed into a similar morphological type. The leukaemic origin and nature of these cells cannot be proved by present experimental methods. Because they have lost the typical morphological appearance of leukaemic cells, their origin by transformation or contamination must be considered.

Confirmation of Osgood's findings, or better still, the isolation of a morphologically stable human leukaemic blast cell strain is still awaited.

Acute leukaemic cells of animals have been cultured *in vitro* for many years in association with fibroblast-like cells (Bichel, 1939; de Bruyn, 1949a; Kieler, 1955) and more recently by themselves (de Bruyn, 1949b; and Fischer, 1957, 1958). It appears from the work of these authors that mouse leukaemic cells have fastidious and exacting nutritional requirements which may be met either by feeder cells or by specially designed media (Haley *et al*, 1961). Given suitable conditions, some cell strains will live and multiply indefinitely *in vitro*. An advantage of studying mouse cells is that their leukaemic properties can be checked by inoculating them into genetically compatible mice. It is not of course possible to check Osgood's human strains by these means. However, it is of some interest that cells of strain J 111 when injected into the hamster cheek pouch produce a tumour which morphologically resembles a human sarcoma. Since mouse leukaemic cells can be cultured continuously in a stable morphological form, there would appear to be no reason why human leukaemic cells could not similarly be cultured if the correct nutritional and other environmental conditions could be provided.

Maturation

The possibility that acute leukaemic cells might mature and differentiate into recognisable cells of the granulocytic, monocytic or lymphocytic cell series has aroused interest from the point of view of the possible use of *in vitro* culture techniques for the classification of acute leukaemia. It is also of some interest in pathogenesis, as it has been argued that maturation would be evidence against the neoplastic nature of the disease, since neoplastic cells do not usually differentiate (Hoogstraten, 1949, 1950; Whitby, 1951). This argument is not altogether convincing, since differentiation is seen in malignant cells of other types in certain circumstances. The evidence concerning the *in vitro* maturation of leukaemic blast cells is conflicting. Some authors have claimed that it occurs, whereas others deny it. Generally, the claims that maturation occurs have been made by authors who have used indirect methods of observation such as total and differential cell counts and examination of histological sections. No evidence of maturation by direct observation has been found.

Maturation of leukaemic haemocytoblasts or 'stem cells' has been described (Timofeevsky and Benevolenskaya, 1927), but not confirmed. Support for the maturation of leukaemic myeloblasts into myelocytes is given by several authors (Sabin *et al*, 1924; Timofeevsky and Benevolenskaya, 1927; Pierce, 1932; Israels, 1940a; Hoogstraten, 1949; and Nowell, 1960a). On the negative side, maturation has been looked for but not seen by many workers (Hirchfeld, 1927; Fieschi and Astaldi, 1946; Fieschi *et al*, 1954; Fieschi *et al*, 1956; Pulvertaft and Humble, 1956; and Woodliff, 1962). Maturation of leukaemic monoblasts has been described by Israels (1940b), who also presented some indirect evidence for the maturation of leukaemic lymphoblasts. Others have not been able to confirm this and consider that maturation does not take place *in vitro*.

Whilst there is considerable evidence that limited maturation of some cell types may take place, it is at present not fully proven due to the inadequacy of the methods of observation which have been used.

Direct observation of a cell from blast stage to mature granulocyte, monocyte or lymphocyte is required before this question can be finally settled.

Transformation

Transformation of acute leukaemic cells has often been described, but again the evidence is usually indirect. Hirchfeld (1927) thought that leukaemic myeloblasts transformed into macrophage-type and fibroblast-like cells; similar results were reported by Timofeevsky and Benevolenskaya (1927) and Pierce (1932). Timofeevsky and

Benevolenskaya further described the transformation of leukaemic myeloblasts into erythroblasts and lymphoblasts. Increased pleomorphism of leukaemic myeloblasts with increases in the number of cells containing Auer bodies and transformation into 'globose' type cells has been described by the Italian School (Fieschi et al, 1956). The transformation of leukaemic monoblasts and promonocytes into macrophage-like cells and giant cells has been described by several authors (Hoogstraten, 1949; Nowell, 1960a). The transformation of leukaemic lymphoblasts has not been described.

General pattern of culture

Observations of the general pattern of culture of leukaemic cells have been made by several authors. Fieschi and his colleagues (1954), using a solid nutrient culture method, found that the outgrowth of leukaemic cells was slow and irregular. Fibroblast-like cells were less evident than in normal cultures and in some 'globose' type cells were found after five days.

Hiraki (Hiraki et al, 1956), using a similar method, found a difference between the growth zone surrounding explants of leukaemic marrows and those surrounding explants of normal marrows. A pattern highly characteristic of leukaemia was described. Fujita and Takino (1960) found more variation in their cultures made by the same method. Analysis showed that the pattern was dependent on the migration of normal cells and the more sluggish leukaemic cells. Varying proportions of these two cell types gave rise to different patterns. Similar findings have been noted in serum agar cultures. However the pattern produced even from replicate cultures of the same specimen were too variable to allow any significant conclusions to be made (Woodliff, 1962). Brooke et al (1958) claimed that a different pattern of culture was given by the three main cytological types of acute leukaemic cells when cultured by a modification of the gradient glass substrate method. However, typical patterns are only found in about eighty per cent of cases (Brooke, 1959). The cultural pattern is usually non-specific in cases where there is difficulty in classification on morphological grounds.

Thus, although claims have been made from time to time that acute leukaemias may be classified according to the behaviour of the cells in tissue culture, none of the methods has proved to be of practical value. The motility, maturation or general pattern of culture of the cells may allow classification, but usually only in cases where this may be readily determined by conventional morphological and cytochemical studies.

GRANULOCYTIC SERIES

Disorders of the cells of this series may be divided into those in which there is a granulocytic leucopenia, those in which there is a reactive granulocytic leucocytosis, and those in which the cells are leukaemic.

Granulocytic leucopenias may follow a lack of granulopoietic cells in the bone marrow (myeloid hypoplasia or aplasia), or a fault in the maturation of such cells or possibly excessive loss in the tissues. Cultures of bone marrow from hypoplastic cases have shown that there is a slower maturation, as well as decreased production of granulocytic cells when compared with normal (Sacchetti and Salvidio, 1957; Fieschi and Sacchetti, 1960). A similar picture is seen in cells from bone marrow showing a maturation arrest; the main difference being a quantitative one in the number of cells present.

Cultures of bone marrow from patients with a granulocytic leucocytosis of short duration resemble those from normal persons. If the condition has been present for some time, increased reproduction but delayed maturation is found in some cases, but in others there is decreased reproduction as well as delayed maturation (Fieschi and Sacchetti, 1959 and 1960).

Cultures of cells from the bone marrow and blood of patients with chronic granulocytic leukaemia have been studied by many authors. The most frequent cell type in this material is the neutrophil myelocyte. Its precursor, the myeloblast, is also usually present, as are eosinophil and basophil myelocytes and more mature cells of the neutrophilic and basophilic series. Studies of these cells *in vitro* have been directed towards their survival and motility, metabolism, multiplication, maturation and transport.

Survival and motility

Cells recognisable as leukaemic myelocytes may survive in cultures for several weeks (Parker and Rhoads, 1928), but no established cell strains have been isolated. They are generally considered to be non-motile, although occasional cells may be seen to show sluggish movement. Cells which migrate from cultures of marrow flecks are usually more mature cells (Avroroff and Timofeevsky, 1914).

Metabolism

The oxygen uptake of chronic granulocytic leukaemia cells has been measured by Bisset and Alexander (1960), whose results for cells from eight cases range from 0·30 to 0·42 μμl/cell/hour (compared with a normal leucocyte range of 0·20 to 0·30 μμl/cell/hour) and by Bicz (1960), whose results for four cases range from 0·19 to 0·23 μμl/cell/hour. These results are in the same range as those obtained by the author, who measured the oxygen uptake of cells from a single patient with chronic granulocytic leukaemia on three different occasions and obtained readings of 0·29, 0·32 and 0·36 μμl/cell/hour. More mature cells from a patient with polycythaemia vera who had a leucocyte count of 33,000/c.mm took up 0·19 μμl/cell/hour. Leucocytes from the peripheral blood of patients with chronic granulocytic leukaemia probably take up more oxygen than those from normal or polycythaemic blood. This change may however only be a reflection of the relative immaturity of the cells in the leukaemic blood.

Autoradiographic and other studies of the *in vitro* metabolism of chronic granulocytic leukaemia cells have failed to show any difference from normal cells of comparable maturity (Lajtha *et al*, 1954; Lajtha, 1957).

Multiplication

Leukaemic myelocytes multiply in many, but not all, types of cell culture (Avroroff and Timofeevsky, 1911; Parker and Rhoads, 1928; Israels, 1940a and b; Gunz, 1948a and b; Woodliff, 1962). Evidence of *in vitro* multiplication has also been obtained from studies of the incorporation of radioactive phosphorus into the deoxyribonucleic acid of such cells (Osgood *et al*, 1951). Morphologically the mitoses resemble those of normal cells, but there is some evidence that cellular multiplication is slower than normal (Sacchetti and Bianchini, 1953b; Salera and Tamburino, 1953; Fieschi and Sacchetti, 1960).

Maturation

There is considerable indirect evidence that limited maturation of leukaemic cells of granulocytic series takes place in some *in vitro* systems. However, in other types of culture such changes have not been found, and direct observation of culture cells does not support the view that maturation is taking place. Avroroff and Timofeevsky (1914) were the first to state that maturation took place in culture, and some confirmation of their work is to be found in the writings of Wallbach (1936), Israels (1940a and b) and Gunz (1948a and b). Other authors have been uncertain as to whether maturation is taking place, and some state that it definitely does not (Osgood, 1940; Woodliff, 1962). The question is not finally settled. It is of some importance, for if agents could be found which would promote maturation, they could conceivably be used in the treatment of chronic granulocytic leukaemia.

Transformation

Descriptions of the transformation of leukaemic cells of the granulocytic series into macrophage-type or fibroblast-like cells are found in the older literature (Avroroff and Timofeevsky, 1914; Hirschfeld, 1927; Caffier, 1927; Pierce, 1932; Wallbach, 1936). Others (Parker and Rhoads, 1928 and Verati, 1928) found such cells in their cultures, but were uncertain as to their origin. All these reports are based on indirect evidence, and direct observation of the transformation of leukaemic granulocytic cells has not been reported.

MONOCYTIC SERIES

Disorders of the cells of this series can be divided into reactive hyperplasias and leukaemic states.

Cell culture studies have not contributed to an understanding of the reactive conditions. Personal experience has shown that cells from such conditions behave like leukaemic monocytic cells.

Leukaemic monoblasts have been described previously (p. 52) and their cultural differentiation from other acute leukaemia cells discussed. Both they and the more mature leukaemic promonocytes and monocytes can survive for many weeks, and they have a characteristic motility. Another prominent characteristic is their great power of phagocytosis; ingested debris and vacuoles are frequently found in such cells. Studies of their metabolism have not been made. Multiplication has not been seen by the author, but is described by Israels (1940b), who also considered that maturation takes place *in vitro*. Many different cell types are seen in cultures of cells from patients with monocytic leukaemia and these may be due to transformations. The established cell strains (J 96 and J 111) isolated from the peripheral blood of patients with monocytic leukaemia by Brooke and Osgood (1959) may also be transformed cells.

LYMPHOCYTIC SERIES

Disorders of the cells of this series can be divided into reactive hyperplasias and into acute and chronic leukaemic states.

Reactive hyperplasias of the lymphoid cells have not been the subject of study by tissue culture methods, and acute lymphoblastic leukaemia cells have been discussed above. Cells from cases of chronic lymphocytic leukaemia have been studied by many workers. The predominant cell type in this material is the mature lymphocyte, which may be either large or small. A lesser number of lymphoblasts may also be present. Studies of these cells *in vitro* have been directed towards their survival and motility, metabolism, multiplication and transformation.

Survival and motility

Human leukaemic lymphocytes may survive for several days *in vitro* (Parker and Rhoads, 1928; Pilati and Pinelli, 1936). Cultures of both normal and leukaemic lymphoblasts show an exponential decline in the numbers of viable cells with time (Jago, 1961) and there seems to be little difference between them in this respect. For example, Schrek (1958a and b and Schrek *et al*, 1958) found that 10 per cent of normal blood lymphocytes survived in his culture system for 8–9 days and 10 per cent of leukaemic lymphocytes survived for 9–11 days. The only report of continuous culture of chronic lymphocytic leukaemia cells is that of Brooke and Osgood (1959) mentioned below. Leukaemic lymphocytes resemble normal lymphocytes in their motility; they show the typical 'hand mirror' forms.

Metabolism

Metabolic studies of lymphocytic luekaemia cells have been made by several groups (Bicz, 1960; Bisset and Alexander, 1960; Woodliff, 1962) who have measured the oxygen uptake *in vitro*. The results are in general agreement, ranging from 0·11 to 0·37 $\mu\mu$l/cell/hour. These are of the same order, but within the lower range, as normal mixed leucocytes. It has not been possible to separate sufficient quantities of normal lymphocytes to allow a direct comparison between the two.

Multiplication

Lymphocytic leukaemia cells are generally regarded as end cells which do not multiply. In support of this are the experiments of Osgood *et al* (1951) who cultured cells from three patients with chronic lymphocytic leukaemia and found that there was no significant uptake of 32_p over ten days. They considered that the cells were not multiplying.

However, Brooke and Osgood (1959) have reported on the isolation of a cell strain (M 166, J 111) from the blood of a patient with chronic lymphocytic leukaemia. In this culture, areas of cellular growth resembling cords of a lymph node medulla were seen. Whether the cells that were actually multiplying were small lymphocytes is doubtful.

Transformation

There are several reports in the literature on the transformation potential of chronic lymphocytic leukaemic cells. Avroroff and Timofeevsky (1915) reported that they changed into macrophage and fibroblast-like cells. Support for these observations is given by Silberberg and Voit (1931) and Timofeevsky and Benevolenskaya (1929). Other workers have noted such cells in similar cultures (Hirschfeld, 1927; Hirschfeld and Klee-Rawidowicz, 1928; Pierce, 1932) but believed they came from monocytes present in the explant rather than from the lymphocytes. No direct observations on the transformation of such cells have been recorded.

PLASMOCYTIC SERIES

Disorders of the cells of this series can be divided into reactive hyperplasias and neoplastic conditions. Few studies have been made of their behaviour *in vitro*. Marrow from patients with myelomatosis has been observed on serum agar by Pulvertaft and Humble (1956) and by the author. The malignant plasma cells live for one to three days. Attempts by the author to demonstrate the *in vitro* production of Bence-Jones protein by such cells in glass substrate cultures failed.

MEGAKARYOCYTE-THROMBOCYTIC SERIES

Disorders of cells of this series can be divided into hypoplastic and anaplastic states, into reactive hyperplasias and into neoplastic conditions. Most *in vitro* studies have been concerned with idiopathic thrombocytopenic purpura. In this condition there are reduced numbers of thrombocytes in the blood but the marrow may contain numerous megakaryocytes. Some defect of maturation of these cells is postulated. Hiraki (1958) cultured the marrow from five cases both before and after splenectomy. Before the operation the megakaryocytes showed neither motility nor tentacle formation, whereas after the operation they became mobile, showed a striking formation of tentacles and thrombocyte formation due to separation of cytoplasm from the ends of the tentacles. Izak and Nelken (1957) also studied cultures of marrow from cases of idiopathic thrombocytopenic purpura. They found greatly accelerated break-down of the megakaryocytes and the thrombocytes produced soon showed degenerative changes. They were agglutinated and phago-cytosed by myeloid and reticulum cells in the cultures.

Sacchetti and Bianchini (1955) found that there was increased mitotic activity of the nucleus of megakaryocytes from patients with thrombocytopenia when compared with normal. However, in reactive thrombocytosis the *in vitro* behaviour of the megakaryocyte was found to be normal.

Malignant megakaryocytes do not appear to have been cultured *in vitro*.

Further cell culture studies of factors influencing thrombopoiesis, such as thrombopoietin and antibodies directed against throm-bocytes, might well be worth while.

ERYTHROCYTIC SERIES

Disorders of the cells of this series can be divided into the anaemias and the neoplastic disorders. The anaemias can be further divided into those due to excessive blood loss – the haemorrhagic and haemolytic – and those due to impaired production of blood due to nutritional deficiency or failure of the bone marrow. In some cases both factors operate.

Cell culture studies of marrow from cases of uncomplicated haemorrhagic anaemias merely show increased erythroblastic activity. More extensive studies have been made on cells from patients with various haemolytic anaemias.

Auto-immune haemolytic anaemia

In this condition, antibodies in the plasma react against the patient's own erythrocytes, causing their premature destruction. Cultures of marrow from such patients show a markedly decreased rate of erythrocyte production; this is improved if normal compatible serum is added (Rossi *et al*, 1957; Sacchetti *et al*, 1958; Fieschi and Sacchetti, 1960). Although the marrow from such patients appears hyperplastic, it seems likely that the antibodies are interfering with this compensatory mechanism to make it less effective. Sera from such patients inhibits *in vitro* erythropoiesis of normal marrow.

Thalassaemia

This condition is classified with the haemolytic anaemias as there is a decreased survival of erythrocytes in the peripheral blood. How-ever, it could also be included as a failure of the bone marrow as there is evidence of ineffective erythropoeisis. The rate of useful erythrocyte production is inadequate and there is evidence of poor haemoglobin synthesis (Bannerman, 1961). Cell culture studies using bone marrow have shown that there is an increased mitotic activity of the erythroblasts in this condition (Astaldi *et al*, 1951, Astaldi and Tolentino, 1952). However, maturation is always retarded; a finding confirmed using a different method of culture by Berman and Powsner (1959). Normal sera do not correct this defect and sera from patients with thalassaemia do not cause a decrease in the multiplication of normal erythroblasts *in vitro*. This finding indicates that the defect lies in the cells themselves. Experiments using peripheral blood reticulocytes from patients with thalassaemia and employing radioactive precursors have indicated that there is a defect in haem synthesis (Bannerman *et al*, 1959). This may be one of the primary lesions, or alternatively the primary defect may be in globin chain production (Itano, 1953, Ingram and Stretton, 1959).

Iron deficiency anaemias

Studies of the bone marrow cultures have shown that there is an increased mitotic activity but decreased maturation of erythroblasts in simple iron deficiency anaemias. The addition of normal serum improves the maturation rate, suggesting that the iron it contains may hasten the development of previously iron deficient cells. Iron deficient plasma does not slow the maturation of normal cells; presumably because they contain sufficient iron for their immediate needs (Astaldi *et al*, 1950; Berman and Powsner, 1959).

In hookworm anaemia, both mitotic activity and maturation are decreased (Trincao *et al*, 1952). The significance of this is uncertain, but both defects are partially corrected by normal plasma. Possibly some other factor, as well as iron, is deficient in the plasma of patients with hookworm anaemia.

Folic acid and cobalamin deficiency anaemias

A deficiency in the diet, failure of absorption, or interference with the metabolism of folic acid and cobalamin (vitamin B_{12}) co-factors leads to megaloblastic erythropoiesis and anaemia. Extensive studies have been made into this type of anaemia using cell culture techniques. The main interest has been to find out which chemicals will convert megaloblastic into normoblastic erythropoiesis. By such experiments, it should be possible to find the substance which actually affects the cells. Other compounds, active *in vivo*, might act indirectly by promoting the synthesis or activating a necessary metabolite. Megaloblastic erythropoiesis *in vitro* is slower than normal (Fieschi and Astaldi, 1945), but this can be partially or wholly corrected by a variety of substances, including normal serum, liver extracts and folic acid (Rusznyák *et al*, 1947 and 1948; Astaldi *et al*, 1948; Astaldi and Tolentino, 1949). Further experiments confirmed the effect of folic acid and demonstrated that folinic acid is also active in this respect (Callender and Lajtha, 1951; Franco and Arkun, 1951; Lajtha, 1952; Thompson, 1952; Swan *et al*, 1955). There is some variation to be found in the results of adding cobalamins (vitamin B_{12}). Whilst Sacchetti and Perreira (1952) and Swan *et al* (1955) found that megaloblasts were converted at least partially to normoblasts, many other groups have found such preparations to be ineffective. The addition of gastric juice or intrinsic factor to a cobalamin preparation has enhanced its activity in some hands but not in others. The question of the activity of cobalamins *in vitro* therefore remains unsettled, but the recent discovery of active cobalamin co-enzymes will probably lead to further experiments and clarification of the position.

Some workers (Lajtha, 1950; Thompson, 1950) have found that normal marrow grown in pernicious anaemia serum has become megaloblastic. An inhibitory factor in such sera was postulated, but attempts by others to confirm this finding have been unsuccessful (Feinmann *et al*, 1952; Thomas and Lochte, 1957; Swan *et al*, 1955). Niacynamide has been found to increase the rate of maturation of megaloblastic bone marrow *in vitro*, but not to convert it to normoblastic (Astaldi and Baldini, 1950).

Idiopathic hypoplastic anaemias

Cell culture studies have not contributed to our understanding of those cases of anaemia characterised by a lack of erythroblasts in the bone marrow. The erythroblasts that are present appear to behave normally *in vitro*. More extensive studies have been made in anaemias due to uraemia.

Uraemic anaemia

Cell culture studies of erythroblasts of patients with uraemia show a decreased mitotic activity and maturation (Sacchetti, 1953; Markson and Rennie, 1956; Berman and Powsner, 1959). Furthermore, uraemic sera inhibit the maturation of normal erythroblasts, and normal sera enhance the activity of uraemic erythroblasts, confirming that the defect in uraemia is humoral rather than cellular.

F

Polycythaemia vera

The erythroblasts of patients with polycythaemia vera behave like those of control subjects *in vitro* (Bernardelli *et al*, 1952). However, polycythaemic plasma has a stimulating effect, promoting the maturation of both normal and polycythaemic erythroblasts (Berman and Powsner, 1959). This may be related to its increased erythropoietin activity (see later p. 76).

Erythraemias

Malignant neoplastic changes of the erythroid cells are found in the erythroleukaemias and the chronic and acute erythraemias (Di Guglielmo's syndrome). Few *in vitro* studies of such cells have been made. Blackburn and Lajtha (1951) cultured cells from a case of erythroleukaemia and found that some of the erythroblasts, including some with megaloid features, matured. It would be of interest to culture cells from further cases and to study the effects of drugs on the metabolism of the cells. However, these conditions are relatively uncommon and opportunities for such studies are therefore rare.

OTHER MARROW CELLS

The disorders of other cells in the blood and bone marrow have not
The disorder of other cells in the blood and bone marrow have not been systematically investigated by cell culture methods. Occasionally carcinoma cells in such material may grow *in vitro* and this is a possible source of some established cell strains derived from such material (Berman *et al*, 1955).

TRANSFORMED AND ALTERED CELLS

McCulloch *et al* (1956) obtained an established fibroblast-like cell found in cultures of bone marrow from patients with disorders of haemopoiesis.

McCulloch *et al* (1956) obtained an established fibroblast-like cell strain from three cases of leukaemia. McCulloch and Parker (1956) considered that they were transformed cells and suggested that Osgood's leukaemic cell strains were similar transformed cells and not leukaemic at all. Subsequently, Parker's cells were shown to be contaminating mouse cells of Earle's L strain (Rothfels *et al*, 1959). The origin of Osgood's strain is not certain; they may represent transformation or contaminating cells, a point which has been discussed previously (p. 57).

Berg and Rosenthal (1961) isolated fibroblast-like cells from normal and leukaemic bone marrows using human amnion cells as a feeder layer. No differences in the morphology, type of degeneration, rate of metabolism or viral susceptibility were found. This confirms and amplifies the previous observation that no differences could be found in the second and third phases of glass substrate cultures as prepared from leukaemic and non-leukaemic bone marrows (Woodliff, 1958a). Further confirmation that fibroblast-like cells from leukaemic marrow resemble those from normal marrow has recently been presented by Ang *et al* (1962), who isolated the cells directly in Leighton tube cultures. No cytological differences were seen and they found no evidence of viral cytopathogenicity.

CHAPTER 6

The effect of nutrients and stimlants on cell cultures

The methods of culture reviewed in Chapter 2 all provide for contact between the cells and a nutrient fluid. This fluid is needed to provide essential substances for cell maintenance and growth. These include inorganic ions, amino acids, lipids, carbohydrates, proteins, water and oxygen. They also make provision for the control of hydrogen ion concentration and provide macromolecules which are necessary for the healthy maintenance of most cells *in vitro*.

Most media have been designed to resemble body fluids, so that the change in environment of the cells from *in vivo* to *in vitro* is as small as possible. As a means to this end, body fluids are frequently used, usually diluted with a balanced salt solution resembling extracellular fluid. Such media are essential for the primary isolation of cells. In recent years a number of artificial media have been designed to partly or wholly replace body fluids. These have the advantage of being defined; unlike body fluids their composition is known and can be reproduced regularly. Two in common use, Eagle's medium and medium 199, are further described in appendix A. Unfortunately, blood and bone marrow cells will not grow in these media alone; nevertheless, they are valuable when used with serum.

Some of the artificial media will support the growth of established cell strains (Fischer, 1958; Waymouth, 1959), and it appears that each type of cell has different nutritional requirements. Concentrations of one substance which may be ideal for certain types of cells may be inhibitory for another, and this makes the provision of a universal medium difficult if not impossible. It seems likely that each type of blood and bone marrow cell has different requirements, and that those suitable for multiplication may not favour maturation. Until such factors are further defined therefore, the choice of a medium will be arbitrary. Generally speaking, medium 199 and serum are useful starting points. The different factors in nutrition, inorganic ions, body fluids, tissue extracts, amino acids, lipids, carbohydrates, nucleotides, vitamins and co-enzymes, are further discussed below, followed by an account of substances which stimulate growth *in vitro*.

INORGANIC IONS

It is generally accepted that sodium, potassium, magnesium, phosphates, carbonates and bicarbonates are essential for the maintenance of cells *in vitro*. These substances are present in concentrations similar to those found in the body fluids in all the physiological salines used in cell culture studies, including those described by Tyrode (1910), Earle (1943), White (1946), Hanks (1948), Gey (1949), and Krebs (Bisset and Alexander, 1960). These fluids, which are also called balanced salt solutions, resemble plasma in their tonicity and therefore can be used to dilute body fluids used as culture media, without upsetting the osmotic equilibrium of the cells. They also have a hydrogen ion concentration similar to plasma and by their buffering action help to maintain cultures at a suitable pH. In some solutions this is based mainly on phosphate ions, but in others bicarbonate buffering is used. The latter requires an atmosphere containing $3 - 5$ per cent CO_2 for adjustment of the pH to suitable levels. Dextrose is usually added as a source of nutritional carbohydrate. The compositions of Earle's, Hanks' and Krebs' solutions are given in appendix A. Care is required in their preparation; often it is more convenient to buy them ready made. Phenol red is frequently added as a pH indicator, and seems to have no deleterious effect on the cells in the low concentrations used.

The use of any of the above, or similar solutions, can be recommended. As there is no evidence that any one is superior, that found most convenient to the individual cell culturist is usually used.

The benefit of adding trace ions to culture media has not been fully explored. Waymouth (1960) found that traces of iron, copper, manganese, zinc, cobalt and molybdenum promoted the health of strain L cells *in vitro*. Iron is present in some of the artificial media, such as media 199 and 858 (Morgan *et al*, 1950; Healey *et al*, 1955), and in White's (1949) medium for chick heart muscle. Other media do not contain it. Osgood (1939a) mentioned that iron in his medium might have some beneficial effect on his cultures of blood and bone marrow cells. Studies of other ions do not appear to have been made; it would be of interest to study the effect of trace elements of haematological interest – copper, cobalt, zinc, chromium and molybdenum – on blood and bone marrow cells *in vitro*.

BODY FLUIDS

Blood and bone marrow cells cultured in simple salt solutions may live for some time, but they cannot be maintained at 37°C for long periods without deterioration. Growth either does not occur or is very poor under such conditions. The addition of body fluids causes an immediate improvement (Norris and Majnarich, 1948a and b; Biesele and Berger, 1950; Woodliff, 1958a). The early cell culturists used clotted lymph or plasma; subsequently serum or serous exudates have been used. These fluids are such complex mixtures of proteins and other chemicals, that it is difficult to determine which of the substances present are most beneficial. They contain macromolecules, and there is some evidence that this physical property promotes the health of cells *in vitro*. They also contain many nutrients in the form of peptides, amino acids, lipids and carbohydrates, as well as minor factors. For most purposes, pooled normal adult human serum can be used. This should be heat inactivated to remove the activity of any antibodies and Seitz filtered. Occasional batches are cytotoxic, and if possible all sera should be pretested by adding them to established cell strains. Umbilical cord blood is used by some authors and is said to be non-toxic; however it is not readily available in large quantities. In cultures of animal cells it may be possible to use sera from another species, for example calf serum, in the media used to culture marrow cells. Heterologous sera have not been used in media used for human blood and bone marrow cell cultures. In experiments designed to test the growth promoting or inhibiting factors in serum, the natural sera are compared with the subject's own serum for an effect on the cells *in vitro*. For example, serum from patients with uraemia inhibits the maturation of erythroblasts (p. 67).

TISSUE EXTRACTS

Carrel (1913) found that tissue extracts were effective in promoting the growth of cells *in vitro*. Embryo extract was found to be the best and its effect is thought to be due to unidentified labile nutrient factors. Some of these are of low molecular weight, as ultrafiltrates of such extracts have a growth promoting effect in certain circumstances (Sanford *et al*, 1952).

Various extracts have been added to blood and bone marrow cell cultures, but with no clear results which would favour their routine use. Jeney (1932) reported that the spleen and liver extracts were favourable for the formation of normoblasts in cultures of rabbit bone marrow, and Rachmilewitz and Rosin (1944) claimed that red cell stroma increased the rate of proliferation of red cell precursors in their cultures.

However, chicken embryo extract did not stimulate the erythropoietic activity of human bone marrow cultures in one series of experiments (Astaldi *et al*, 1951); neither did it have any appreciable effect on any of the cells in serum agar or glass substrate cultures (Woodliff, 1962).

PROTEINS

Body fluids containing protein are usually required for the healthy maintenance and growth of cells *in vitro*. The protein is thought to act physically as a macromolecule and as a source of amino acids. Experiments performed with dialysed serum, which contains only the large protein molecules, have shown that it will support the growth of certain cells when fortified with artificial media containing amino acids. Similarly, purified albumin can be tried as a replacement for serum. These media represent an approach to the protein-free media which will support the growth of a few specialised cell strains, and are of great value in metabolic experiments where it is desirable to know the concentration of each constituent.

Blood and bone marrow cells will not survive for long periods without protein. If albumin is used with medium 199, better results are obtained than with medium 199 alone; however they are both inferior to the use of serum and medium 199 (Woodliff, 1958a).

AMINO ACIDS

Amino acids and peptides may be obtained by cells in culture by proteolysis of protein present in the medium. They are required for protein synthesis by the cells. Alternately, they may be added. A relatively cheap and convenient source available commercially is lactalbumin hydrolysate. This mixture appears to encourage the growth of some cell strains and is extensively used for the growth of cells for virus studies. However, it does not produce any appreciable effect on serum agar and glass substrate cultures of blood and bone marrow cells (Woodliff, 1962). The common artificial media contain balanced quantities of amino acids. Eagle's media (appendix A) contain twelve amino acids needed by HeLa and L cells. These are – *l*-Arginine, *l*-Cystine, *l*-Histidine, *l*-Isoleucine, *l*-Leucine, *l*-Lysine, *l*-Methionine, *l*-Phenylalanine, *l*-Threonine, *l*-Tryptophan, *l*-Tyrosine, *l*-Valine. Medium 199 (Appendix A) contains twenty amino acids, but they are probably not all essential for each cell type. Excess of amino acids can be inhibitory, and it is probable that different types of cells have different optimal requirements of amino acid concentrations. It is already established that epithelial-like cells and fibroblast-like cells have different requirements, and it seems likely that similar circumstances apply to the different types of bone marrow cells. Few studies of these have been made; however Baldini and Sacchetti (1953) found that leucocytes in bone marrow cultures deficient in *l*-cysteine and *l*-cystine degenerated rapidly. Addition of either amino acid to the media had a protective effect, especially on the granulocytes.

LIPIDS

Many cells can grow in the absence of added fats, fatty acids and related substances. However, the more complex artificial media, such as medium 199, contain cholesterol and several fat soluble substances which are stabilized in solution by the addition of the detergent tween 80. The value of substances of this group in the *in vitro* maintenance and multiplication of blood and bone marrow cells has not been investigated.

CARBOHYDRATES

Most media contain glucose as a source of energy and it is an essential nutrient for many cell types. A few cell strains are known which will utilise pentoses and lactose for some time, but eventually degeneration occurs (Chang, 1960). The utilisation of carbohydrates other than glucose by blood and bone marrow cells has not been investigated.

NUCLEOTIDES

Various polynucleotides, mononucleotides, purine and pyrimidine compounds have been tested for stimulatory effects in a variety of cell systems; some have been found to be inhibitory (Biesele *et al*, 1955). Such compounds have not been tested in blood and bone marrow cell cultures.

VITAMINS AND CO-ENZYMES

Eagle (1955a and b) studied the effect of vitamins on the *in vitro* maintenance of HeLa and L cells. He found that choline, nicotinic acid, pantothenic acid, pyridoxal, riboflavin, thiamine, inositol, biotin and folic acid were essential. If any one of these was omitted from the medium the cells degenerated. Many of the artificial media contain even more compounds of this nature. In blood and bone marrow cell cultures interest has centered on the haemopoietic vitamins especially folic acid and cobalamins (vitamin B_{12}).

Folic acid is probably required for growth by all cell types in culture and is a constituent of all artificial media. Jacobson (1954b) has demonstrated that one of its active forms, folinic acid, is required for the completion of mitosis in fibroblast-like cells.

Unlike folic acid, the cobalamins are not required for the growth of HeLa and L cells and are not added to artificial media. Hiraki (1961) however believes that cyanocobalamin has a beneficial effect on cultures of bone marrow; the medium he uses for culture consists of one drop of vitamin B_{12} (100 µg/ml) and one drop of serum. Such high concentrations have, however, been without any appreciable effect in other hands (Woodliff, 1961). Most of the studies of folic acid and cobalmins on bone marrow cells *in vitro* have been concerned with their effects on megaloblastic erythropoiesis; they have been summarised previously (p. 66).

GASES

Cells *in vitro* obtain the energy for their metabolic process either by glycolysis or respiration. Glycolysis does not require the presence of oxygen but is a relatively inefficient source of energy and leads to the production of large amounts of pyruvic and lactic acids. For long-term cultures it is therefore desirable to provide oxygen for respiration. The oxygen reaching the cells is dissolved in the medium and when used up must be replaced by diffusion from the atmosphere into the fluid. The provision of a gas phase in contact with the fluid medium is therefore desirable. Commonly air is used or a mixture containing 20 per cent oxygen and 5 per cent CO_2. Either absence of oxygen or very high concentrations are deleterious to blood and bone marrow cell cultures (Woodliff, 1958a). Pulvertaft (1958) has however found that anoxia stimulates platelet formation (p. 46).

Bicarbonate ions and carbon dioxide are necessary for the health of cells and for normal respiration. Usually sufficient carbon dioxide is produced by the cells as a by-product of respiration or the small quantities in the air suffice. However some media, based on Earle's salt solution, require an atmosphere of 3–5 per cent CO_2 for maintenance of a physiological hydrogen ion concentration. This is because they contain a relatively high concentration of bicarbonate for buffering purposes.

The effect of other gases has not been studied. Nitrogen is usually used as an inert substance to make up the balance in studies on the effect of different concentrations of oxygen and carbon dioxide.

HORMONES

Hormones are not usually added to artificial media and there is no evidence that they are required for maintenance and growth of cells *in vitro*.

Attempts have been made to see if they will stimulate the growth of blood and bone marrow cells *in vitro*, and particular interest has centred on the haemopoietic hormones – thrombopoietin, leucopoietin and erythropoietin. Thrombopoietin and leucopoietin (which are thought to stimulate thrombopoiesis and leucopoiesis respectively) are as yet not clearly defined, but it is to be hoped that cell culture studies will allow an analysis of their mechanisms of action and possibly be suitable for assay purposes.

Erythropoietin has been more extensively studied. It is a substance produced in response to anoxia which stimulates erythrocyte production. Anoxia itself does not stimulate bone marrow cells *in vitro*. However, serum from anoxic subjects does, and this property can be attributed to its erythropoietic content. Several methods have been developed to assay erythropoietin, usually using experimental animals (Gordon, 1960). An *in vitro* assay would be valuable and attempts in this direction have been made by several groups. Anoxic sera increase the proliferative activity of erythroid cells in bone marrow cell suspension cultures, increase their radioactive iron uptake, and promote erythropoiesis in well cultures of bone marrow (Matoth *et al*, 1958; Schroeder *et al*, 1958; Reisner, 1959). Some correlation between the erythropoietic content and these parameters

PLATE 3 PHA TREATED CULTURE

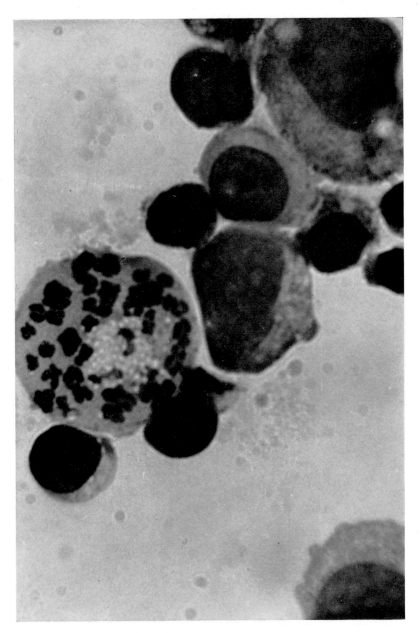

Mitotic figure and cells from a PHA treated culture of peripheral blood leucocytes, spread chromosomes and karyotype.
3a Mitotic figure, altered cells and unaltered lymphocytes from a 3-day PHA culture of normal peripheral blood leucocytes.

PLATE 3 PHA TREATED CULTURE

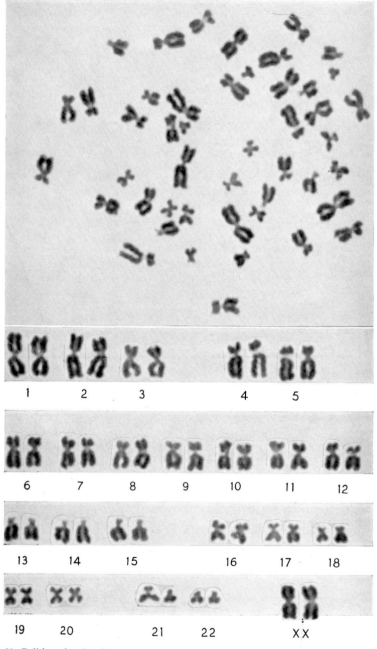

3b Cell in mitosis with spread chromosomes and normal female karyotype.

was obtained but the techniques have not yet been sufficiently well developed to allow their routine use.

PHYTOHAEMAGGLUTININ

Nowell (1960b) recently found that phytohaemagglutinin, a muco-protein extract from red beans (*Phaseolus vulgaris*), stimulated the mitosis of cells in cultures of normal peripheral blood. Such extracts prepared by Rigas (Rigas and Osgood, 1955) were originally used by Osgood and his associates (Osgood, 1955; Osgood and Krippaehne, 1955; Osgood and Brooke, 1955) to agglutinate and thus precipitate the red cells in leukaemic blood and bone marrow cell samples so that the leucocytes could be separated for gradient cultures. Nowell (1960b), using a similar technique, noted that mitosis also occurred in cultures of normal peripheral blood cells. He subsequently investigated the conditions in his cultures to see which factors were responsible for promoting mitosis and found that only those treated with phytohaemagglutinin contained mitoses. Such factors as oxygen tension, carbon dioxide tension and plasma concentration had only minor quantitative effects. As a result of these experiments he postulated that phytohaemagglutinin was a specific initiator of mitosis in cultures of normal human leucocytes. The mitoses were not usually seen until the third day of culture and he suggested that phytohaemagglutinin in some way altered mono-cytes and large lymphocytes so that after a latent period they became capable of division.

This finding has been amply confirmed and has been widely used in human cytogenetic studies (Hungerford *et al*, 1959; Nowell and Hungerford, 1960; Baikie *et al*, 1960; Lennox, 1961; Johnston, *et al*, 1961).

A variety of minor modifications of the original technique have been made (Moorhead *et al*, 1960; Ferguson-Smith *et al*, 1960). It is recommended that the red cells be first precipitated with dextran and phytohaemagglutinin added to the leucocyte suspension later. Using this method, mitotic indices varying from three to sixty-three per thousand following the addition of demecokine were found in the treated cultures and none were found in the untreated cultures (Woodliff, 1962; Plate 3).

Some studies have shown that not all batches of phytohaemag-glutinin are mitogenically active (Nowell, 1961) and Difco now market two preparations. Bacto–Phytohaemagglutinin P is a purified protein phytohaemagglutinin from which the polysaccharide molecules have been removed. It is said to have a powerful haemagglutinating property but to be poor as a mitotic stimulant. Bacto-Phytohaemagglutinin M, the less purified product, is recommended for mitotic studies (Difco Laboratories commercial literature, 1961). It has been reported that this substance is ineffective (de la Chapelle, 1961), but personal experience has shown it to be active. Possibly different batches vary in this respect. Some workers have prepared their own extracts from the red beans (Marshall and Capon, 1961; Cooper et al, 1961). Marshall and Capon suggested that until more is known about the structure of plant substances which exhibit mitogenic activity they should be known as phytomitogens.

Cooper et al studied DNA synthesis in phytohaemagglutinin (PHA) treated cultures. Without treatment only about 0·1 per cent of peripheral blood leucocytes took up tritiated thymidine. Under the influence of PHA there was a sharp rise in labelled cells at twenty-four hours and at seventy hours about fifty per cent were labelled. Confirmation that DNA synthesis was taking place was obtained from microdensimetric measurements of cellular DNA in Feulgen stained preparations. Radioactively labelled cells all contained more than diploid, and up to quadruploid amounts of DNA.

It is not known for certain which peripheral blood cell type undergoes mitosis in these cultures. Because of the comparatively large numbers present and the fact that synthesis and division occur in many cells at the same time, they must be present in large numbers. The small percentage of potentially mitotic cells found in untreated cultures cannot therefore be responsible.

The granulocytes can be excluded on the grounds that mitoses are found in preparations in which these cells are virtually excluded (Woodliff, 1962). Also, degenerating granulocytes are found in most cultures with no intermediate forms.

Nowell suggested that monocytes and large lymphocytes were the cells responsible. Mitoses are found in preparations containing very few monocytes and no intermediate forms between them and mitotic cells are seen in these cultures. However, forms intermediate between lymphocytes and the 'altered' cell which undergoes mitosis, can readily be found. Probably the lymphocytes are in some way altered by the phytomitogens so that DNA synthesis and subsequent mitosis may take place. Cytochemical studies are consistent with this hypothesis, which however has not yet been proved. Not all lymphocytes are stimulated by these substances. Trowell added phytohaemagglutinin to cultures of rat lymph nodes with no effect (1961a).

CHAPTER 7

The effect of cytotoxic therapeutic agents on cell cultures

Cell cultures are being increasingly used to study the effect of known or potential anti-cancer agents. These studies are generally designed to test the effects of drugs on established cell strains (Eagle and Foley, 1956 and 1958) or on freshly isolated fibroblast-like cells and neoplastic cells (Biesele, 1954, 1956 and 1958). Comparatively few studies have been made on blood and bone marrow cells. In this chapter, only agents used in the treatment of proliferative haematological disorders will be reviewed; particular emphasis will be given to their action on blood and bone marrow cell cultures. The drugs concerned are the purine and pyrimidine antagonists, the folic acid antagonists, alkylating agents, hormones and miscellaneous cytotoxic drugs. A final section reviews the effect of ionizing radiations on cells *in vitro*.

PURINE AND PYRIMIDINE ANTAGONISTS

Purine and pyrimidine bases form part of the polynucleotides of both deoxyribonucleic acid and ribonucleic acid proteins. Since these substances are synthesised by rapidly growing tissues, it was thought that interference with this synthesis might inhibit growth. A number of antimetabolites of possible chemotherapeutic value were therefore synthesised and tested. It was found that the purine antagonists were generally more effective than the pyrimidine antagonists. The first drug to be used clinically was 2,6–diaminopurine. This was soon replaced by the more effective compound 6–mercaptopurine (Elion *et al*, 1952; Burchenal *et al*, 1953). The structural formula of this compound, of the natural purine adenine and two other antimetabolites which have been used clinically, 6–chlorpurine and thioguanine, are illustrated in fig. 5.

Although the purine bases of nucleotides are synthesised in the body from small units, there is evidence that some preformed precursors are incorporated into the molecules. It is thought that the incorporation of an abnormal purine in place of the natural compound produces an ineffective nucleotide which in turn leads to disordered cell metabolism and eventual cell death.

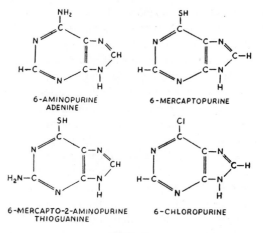

6-AMINOPURINE
ADENINE

6-MERCAPTOPURINE

6-MERCAPTO-2-AMINOPURINE
THIOGUANINE

6-CHLOROPURINE

FIG. 5

THE STRUCTURAL FORMULAE OF THE NATURAL
PURINE, ADENINE, AND THREE PURINE
ANTAGONISTS

The action of this group of drugs *in vitro* has been studied more especially by Biesele (1954b, 1955), who cultured both normal and malignant mouse tissues in the same tube. After twenty-four hours' exposure to 6–mercaptopurine, mitosis of explanted sarcoma 180 cells was inhibited rather more than mitosis of fibroblasts from explanted embryonic skin. Thioguanine inhibited mitosis in both normal and malignant cells to the same extent. The addition of cysteine or cystine to cultures containing 1 mM 6–mercaptopurine increased the mitotic inhibition of embryonic fibroblasts to such an extent that the selective action against sarcoma 180 cells was no longer evident. Biesele concluded that whilst 6–mercaptopurine inhibited mitosis, the extent to which this occurred depended on the nutrients and cell types present and might not be directly related to the malignancy of the cells. As well as inhibiting nucleoprotein synthesis, the drug had an effect on mitochondria and co-enzyme A

(Biesele 1955). Concentrations of 1 and 0·5 mM were found to affect his cultures and high concentrations caused severe degenerative changes.

The effects of mercaptopurine on blood and bone marrow cells *in vitro* have been studied by a variety of methods (Woodliff, 1958a, 1961, 1962; Woodliff and Davis, 1960). 1 mM concentrations have no apparent effect on either glass substrate or serum agar cultures. Mitosis was seen to occur in this concentration. 10 mM concentrations inhibited mitosis, both in these systems and in phytohaemagglutinin-treated cultures of peripheral blood leucocytes. 6mM concentrations were found to inhibit the oxygen uptake of normal bone marrow, but not of bone marrow from a patient with leukaemia resistant to mercaptopurine therapy. 2mM concentrations had no effect, and 4 mM concentrations an intermediate effect. Studies of mouse leukaemic cells (L 1210) showed that the oxygen uptake and net gas output of a sensitive strain of cells was inhibited by 10 mM concentrations of the drug. This concentration did not inhibit a resistant strain (L 1210 MPR) (Woodliff, 1960).

Studies of the effect of the drug on the respiration of human leukaemic leucocytes have shown that the response is variable. Five cases of acute leukaemia were studied. The respiration of the cells was not inhibited by 10 mM concentrations in two, and in these patients the leukaemic process failed to respond to the drug. In the other three, 10 mM concentrations caused a depression of respiration; two showed a response to the drug and the third died shortly after the experiment before the response to therapy could be assessed.

10 mM concentrations caused a depression of respiration of chronic lymphocytic leukaemia cells in five out of six experiments. The explanation for the resistance of the cells from one patient is not known; this drug is not used in the treatment of this disorder.

10 mM concentrations also caused depression of respiration of the cells of a patient with chronic granulocytic leukaemia. 6–chloropurine in concentrations of 5 to 10 times that of 6–mercaptopurine had a similar effect on the respiration of leukaemic leucocytes.

There can be no doubt that 6–mercaptopurine and related compounds can inhibit mitosis *in vitro* if given in sufficiently high concentrations and it is generally thought that the action *in vivo* is due to inhibition of nucleoprotein synthesis. The concentrations of drugs used in the *in vitro* experiments are considerably greater than those found in the body fluids of patients undergoing treatment. Nevertheless, there is some evidence that a correlation may be found between the results of *in vitro* tests which measure mitotic inhibition and the effect of drugs in the patient. Further work to develop an *in vitro* sensitivity test of leukaemic cells to mercaptopurine is being undertaken.

The inhibition of oxygen uptake by sensitive but not by resistant cells to selected concentrations of mercaptopurine suggests that such measurements will be of value as a sensitivity test. These experiments are short-term ones in which little or no cellular multiplication is taking place. The mechanism of the inhibition of respiration is not known, but may be due to interference with co-enzymes (co-enzyme A, ATP, DPN) concerned with respiration. Even if the *in vivo* activity of the drug is not due to this action, a correlation between the two is of value in predicting a response to therapy.

FOLIC ACID ANTAGONISTS

Folic acid, or one of its metabolically active forms such as folinic acid, is a necessary co-enzyme in many biochemical reactions. Analogues of these compounds act as antagonists either by interfering with the conversion of folic acid to an active form or by interfering in its metabolic functions. The most effective group of antagonists are the 4-amino derivatives. The structural formulae of folic and folinic acid and two of the most widely used antagonists, aminopterin and amethopterin, are given in fig. 6. Aminopterin is five to ten times more effective weight for weight than amethopterin, both *in vitro* and *in vivo*.

Folic acid antagonists were introduced into clinical practice for the treatment of leukaemia by Farber *et al* (1948) following the observation that folic acid given to children with acute leukaemia appeared to accelerate the disease.

Many studies have been made of their effects on cells *in vitro*. Amongst those described have been an increased phagocytosis of erythrocytes in bone marrow culture (Salis, 1948), inhibition of mouse sarcoma cells (Stock *et al*, 1950) and inhibition of mitosis of bone marrow cells (Albrecht, 1950). Jacobson (1954a and b) made a careful quantitative study of the effects of aminopterin and amethopterin on fibroblast cultures and defined the effect on mitosis. When examined fifteen minutes after exposure to concentrations of aminopterin from 0·5 to 0·05 mM, it was found that a varying

G

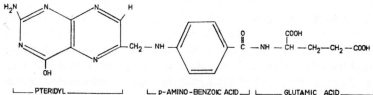

PTERIDYL   p-AMINO-BENZOIC ACID   GLUTAMIC ACID

FOLIC ACID
PTEROYLGLUTAMIC ACID

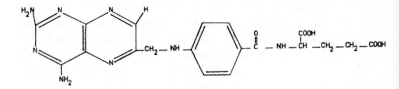

FOLINIC ACID
5-FORMYL 5-6-7-8 TETRAHYDROPTEROYLGLUTAMIC ACID

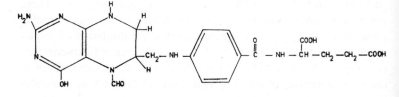

AMINOPTERIN
4-AMINOPTEROYLGLUTAMIC ACID

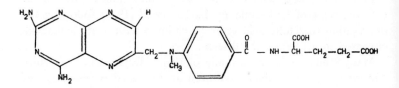

AMETHOPTERIN
4-AMINO-N METHYL PTEROGLUTAMIC ACID

FIG. 6

THE STRUCTURAL FORMULAE OF FOLIC AND FOLINIC
ACIDS AND THEIR ANTAGONISTS

proportion of the cells had become arrested in metaphase. This effect could be reversed by folinic acid but not by folic acid itself. He also found that if the cultures were examined at twenty-four hours, little difference could be found between those treated with antagonists and the controls. This he ascribed to inactivation of the antagonist by the cells. The Kielers (Kieler and Kieler, 1954) tested the effect of amethopterin on cultures of leukaemic cells from mice. They used two strains of cells, both from the same stock but one of which had become resistant to amethopterin. After culture for twenty-four hours they studied the cells and found a significant decrease in the mitotic activity of sensitive cells exposed to 0·022 mM concentrations of amethopterin. A similar effect on resistant cells was obtained only with much higher (2·2 mM) concentrations of the drug.

Studies of the effect of aminopterin on human leukaemic leucocytes were made by Gunz (1950). He found that complete inhibition of mitosis occurred in concentrations of the drug of 0·5 mM and greater. At lower concentrations variable inhibition occurred. Smith (1952) confirmed these results.

In phytohaemagglutinin treated cultures of normal peripheral blood cells, high concentrations (3 mM amethopterin and 0·6 mM aminopterin) of the drugs are required to inhibit mitosis. Lower concentrations (1 mM amethopterin and 0·2 mM aminopterin) inhibited the mitosis of similar cultures of cells from patients with acute leukaemia and with chronic granulocytic leukaemia. Studies are proceeding to see if a useful *in vitro* test of the *in vivo* sensitivity of leukaemic process in patients can be developed from such cultures.

Studies of the effect of the drugs on the *in vitro* respiration of cells have shown that 1 mM amethopterin inhibits the oxygen uptake of normal bone marrow and that taken from a patient with acute leukaemia. 0·2 mM concentrations did not affect normal marrow, but inhibited the respiration of marrow from the patient with acute leukaemia.

Mouse leukaemia cells (L 1210) experiments showed that the oxygen uptake of a sensitive strain of cells was inhibited by 1 mM aminopterin. This concentration of drug did not inhibit a resistant strain (L 1210 AMR).

The same concentration of drug inhibited the oxygen uptake of leukaemic leucocytes from three out of four patients with acute leukaemia. Clinical correlation was not possible, since the anti-folic drugs were not given to these patients.

There can be no doubt that folic acid antagonists inhibit mitosis *in vitro*; there are, however, differences in the literature as to the concentrations and time required for this action. Nor is it yet clear whether measurement of the degree of inhibition will allow the *in vivo* sensitivity of leukaemia to be determined in this way. Although some preliminary experiments suggest that this might be possible, further work is required.

The effect of the antagonists on oxygen uptake of leukaemic cells cannot be explained on the basis of inhibition of mitosis and it is probable that some interference with respiratory metabolism is taking place. The fact that the oxygen uptake of sensitive mouse leukaemic cells is inhibited by concentrations of these compounds which do not affect resistant cells suggests that oxygen uptake measurements may allow the *in vivo* sensitivity of human leukaemic cells to be determined *in vitro*. Further experiments using human cells are required to test this possibility.

ALKYLATING AGENTS

The alkylating agents are a large group of compounds whose biochemical activity is due to their property of reacting with carboxyl, phosphoryl or amino radicals of other compounds and attaching an alkyl radical to them. As a result, the properties of the altered compound are changed and when this occurs to metabolically active substances a disturbance of cellular function may follow, leading to death of the cell. The first compound to be used clinically on a wide scale was nitrogen mustard; its activity depends on the presence of two reactive chlorethyl radicals. Many other compounds varying in their physical and chemical properties have now been prepared. Of these, two are of particular note to haematologists; they are busulphan and chlorambucil, which are used in the treatment of chronic granulocytic and lymphocytic leukaemias respectively.

The effect of alkylating agents on cultures has been studied by several groups.

Nitrogen mustard inhibits mitosis in cultures of bone marrow cells (Albrecht and Boll, 1950) and mouse leukaemia cells (Alexander and Mikulski, 1961). It also has a direct toxic effect on lymphocytes *in vitro* (Schrek, 1948; Trowell, 1960).

Studies of the effect of nitrogen mustard on the respiration of chronic lymphocytic leukaemia cells showed that both 1 and 0·1 mM concentrations caused depression in four experiments in which it was tested (Woodliff and Onesti, unpublished experiments).

Busulphan is poorly soluble and this makes studies of its effects difficult. It had no effect at its limit of solubility on serum agar cultures of bone marrow (Woodliff, 1961). However, 10 mM concentrations in an organic solvent have been found to inhibit the respiration of chronic lymphatic leukaemia cells.

A chemically less stable derivative, dimethyl busulphan, inhibited mitosis in cultured mouse leukaemic cells after a delay of one cell generation (Alexander and Mikulski, 1961). Another derivative, mannitol busulphan, in 10 mM concentrations has not affected the respiration rate of chronic lymphocytic leukaemia cells. Chlorambucil is also poorly soluble, but can be converted into its more soluble sodium salt. Low concentrations (0·3 mM) did not affect the serum agar cultures of bone marrow cells. High concentrations (1 and 10 mM) inhibit the respiration of chronic lymphatic leukaemia cells; 0·1 mM concentrations inhibit it either slightly or not at all. Most cases of chronic lymphatic leukaemia respond to this drug, so the need for an *in vitro* sensitivity test is not great. Nevertheless, studies are proceeding to see if there is any correlation between the concentration of drug required to inhibit respiration of the cells from such patients and the response to treatment.

HORMONES

The main group of hormones used in the treatment of disorders of haemopoiesis are the adrenal steroids and their analogues, typified by cortisone. Corticotrophin, which stimulates the adrenal glands to produce cortisone-like compounds, has a similar biological effect.

The lymphocytolytic effect of these substances has been known for some time (Ingle and Mason, 1938; Wells and Kendall, 1940; Dougherty and White, 1943). It was not until 1949 however when the first ACTH (corticotrophin) Conference was held, that they were established as being of value in the treatment of leukaemia.

They have a definite effect on lymphocytes *in vitro*. Trowell (1953, 1960) found that cortisone was cytocidal for lymphocytes in rat lymph node organ cultures in very low concentrations (0·01 mM), and Schrek (1949) using lymphocyte suspensions found a similar effect. The effect on other cells is less marked. Krippaehne and Osgood (1955) studied the influence of cortisone and hydrocortisone on granulocytes in cultures and found that 0·03 to 0·06 mM concentrations failed to affect the cells over a period of eight days *in vitro*. Nor was there any effect seen in cultures of cells from a patient with eosinophilic leukaemia.

10 mM concentrations of hydrocortisone have a marked, and 1 mM concentrations a mild, depressive effect on the *in vitro* respiration of chronic lymphocytic leukaemia cells. 1 mM concentrations were without effect on the *in vitro* respiration of cells from a patient with chronic granulocytic leukaemia, and 10 mM concentrations had only a mild effect. Further studies to include acute leukaemic cells are needed.

OTHER CYTOTOXIC DRUGS

Urethane
This cytotoxic drug has in the past been used in the treatment of leukaemia and still has a place in the treatment of myelomatosis. *In vitro* it has been found to cause morphological abnormalities, inhibition of mitosis and chromosomal abnormalities in cells of the granulocytic series (Osgood and Chu, 1948; Gunz, 1949; Albrecht and Boll, 1950).

Demecolcine
This drug, which is sometimes used in the treatment of chronic granulocytic leukaemia, is related to colchicine and has a similar effect on cells. In relatively high concentrations (1 mM) these substances have a cytolytic effect (Albrecht, 1955; Woodliff, 1961). In low concentrations (0·001 mM), they arrest mitosis at the metaphase stage without apparently causing any other cytological damage. Advantage of this fact is taken in the stathmokinetic test (Astaldi and Mauri, 1949, 1950) and in cytogenetic studies.

In the stathmokinetic test, mitosis is halted at the metaphase stage and so the numbers present become progressively greater. By counting these, the numbers of cells which would normally undergo cell division can be estimated, thus enabling activity of the various cellular elements of the bone marrow to be compared. It is therefore possible to estimate the multiplication potential of bone marrow cells from different conditions and following the addition of various agents.

In cytogenetic studies, the mitosis of cells in culture is inhibited by three to five hour treatment with demecolcine to cause an accumulation of mitotic figures. The cultures are then treated with a hypotonic solution and prepared for microscopy. Demecolcine treatment should be limited to a few hours, otherwise the chromosomes may be altered morphologically. Some workers prefer not to use it. Since it increases the number of mitoses present in phytohaemagglutinin treated cultures of peripheral blood cells from around one per cent to six per cent, however, the technique is valuable in providing increased numbers of cells suitable for analysis (Woodliff, 1962).

Vincaleukoblastine

This alkaloid, which is an extract from *Vinca rosea*, has been used in the treatment of leukaemia. In cell cultures of J–96, LLC and human embryonic connective tissue cell cultures it was found to have a colchicine-like effect and to act as a metaphase poison (Palmer *et al*, 1960).

IONISING RADIATIONS

Ionising radiations, which are frequently used in the treatment of leukaemia, are so called because their cytotoxic effect is due to the production of highly reactive ions such as free hydrogen atoms and hydroxyl molecules, which react with essential metabolites and alter them chemically. They include roentgen (X) rays and gamma rays, protons, electrons and neutrons which may be released by radioactive isotopes or generated by physical means. Their biological effects are similar so they can be considered together.

The effect of such agents on cell cultures has been extensively studied and they have been found to have both a cytolytic effect and to inhibit mitosis. Much of the earlier work was concerned with the fact that cells which had been irradiated might still multiply. This may however have been due to the fact that some of the cells were not 'hit' by the treatment. Recent advances in quantitative technique have shown that chromosome damage from two to three 'hits' usually prevents a cell from multiplying (Puck, 1958). However the effect is variable, and resistant strains have been developed (Whitfield and Rixon, 1960).

Cultured bone marrow cells other than lymphocytes are not killed by roentgen rays in doses comparable to those used clinically, but their multiplication is inhibited (Osgood and Bracher, 1939; Osgood, 1940; Schrek, 1946a and b). Similarly, the DNA synthesis of such cells is decreased (Lajtha *et al*, 1954, 1958). Inhibition of mitosis of leukaemic cells has also been demonstrated (Gunz, 1949).

Lymphocytes are particularly susceptible to radiation. Several workers have found a marked cytocidal effect on these cells in comparatively low dosages (Schrek, 1946a and b; Trowell, 1952, 1958; Pulvertaft *et al*, 1953). Jago (1961) has compared the effect of roentgen rays on normal and leukaemic lymphocytes. Both were similarly damaged with low doses, but with higher doses the leukaemic cells were more severely affected. The significance of this work is not at present clear, but it is of great interest that differences between different types of normal cells and between normal and leukaemic cells have been described.

CHAPTER 8

Discussion

The review of the literature on blood and bone marrow cell cultures presented in the preceding chapters reveals that *in vitro* studies of these cells have provided useful information about some aspects of normal and pathological haemopoiesis. For the amount of work that has gone into such studies, however, the positive results appear rather meagre. This is due to the limitations of present technical methods. The potential value of cell culture methods is great, and recent advances along several lines suggest that they will be used more frequently in the future.

METHODS

Present methods fall short on one or more of the following requirements: cell multiplication may be limited or non-existent so that the culture dies after a few days or weeks; cell maturation may be limited or not occur at all; recognisable haemopoietic cells may be overgrown by transformed macrophage type or fibroblast-like cells; and statistical evaluation of processes observed qualitatively may be unreliable or impossible. For these reasons, the type of culture used must be carefully selected for each type of problem; no one method is suitable for all experiments.

Whilst seeking to overcome these difficulties, limited advances have been made in recent years with the introduction of several newer methods of culture, each with certain advantages. These have been reviewed in Chapter 2 and their use has allowed some progress to be made.

Further advances in the technique of culture will follow if the cells can be supplied with a suitable nutritional and physical environment. The successful *in vitro* growth of some mouse leukaemic cells indicates that this can be done for one cell type. It now remains to discover the ideal condition for normal blood and bone marrow cells. This may well vary for each cell type, and also differ as to whether multiplication or maturation is required. Suggestions that this will be possible can be found in several recent reports. Reisner (1959) found that maturing cells migrated out of explants in deep culture for several months and that fibroblast-like cells, which he thinks may represent haemocytoblasts, migrated out of explants in shallow cultures. This, and the gradient principles propounded by Osgood (Osgood and Krippaehne, 1955), suggest that variations in oxygen tension or some other factor may be important. Nowell (1960a) found that agitation of his cultures made a difference. Cultures left undisturbed showed some maturation, whereas replicate cultures which were periodically agitated showed multiplication without maturation. Further technical refinements are also needed so that a single cell can be isolated and its multiplication, maturation and transformation potentialities studied. Such studies, which may be feasible using a feeder technique, should allow definite answers to be given to the conflicting claims of cellular transformations found in the older literature.

NORMAL BLOOD AND BONE MARROW CELLS

Cell cultures have revealed little that is new concerning normal haemopoiesis: but they have been valuable in confirming observations made by other methods. They will probably by of value in the assay of haemopoietic stimulating hormones and they have played a very useful role in studies of normal human chromosomes. With perfection in technique more should be learnt from such cultures about the factors which influence normal haemopoiesis. Eventually it may be possible to induce cells to grow and mature *in vitro* for use in replacement therapy. The need for large numbers of viable and functioning haemopoietic cells is great. If a totipotential cell strain could be developed it might be used to repopulate aplastic marrows and to protect from irradiation injury. Such cells have not yet been isolated in tissue culture, though cells with some radiation protective function have been found in mouse bone marrow cell cultures kept at 37°C for up to eleven days (Billen, 1957). Unfortunately, an established transformed cell, isolated from mouse tissue, was unable to protect mice against irradiation injury or to repopulate the thymus (Billen, 1959). The nature of the stem cell is not really known and the transformed cell isolated may have originated from another cell type. Alternatively, its properties may have changed during culture. To produce the large number of stem cells required, the cultured cells would have to undergo many divisions. During this process a mutation to a malignant form might occur, or the cell might lose its beneficial properties. These theoretical obstacles are not insurmountable, but it may be some years before it is possible to infuse patients with such cells. With more mature cells there should be less difficulty. Mature cells, if they can be separated from all cells capable of mitosis, could be given to patients without danger of introducing malignant cells. The production of large numbers of erythrocytes from cultures of erythropoietic cells would be a boon to blood banks. Similarly, infusions of mature thrombocytes might help in bleeding disorders, and infusions of granulocytes and monocytes in certain infections. It might also be possible to establish a clone of cells of the lymphocytic series producing a specific antibody for infusion into patients requiring such an antibody to combat infection or malignant cells. The possibilities are immense, and it is hoped that some of them will be realised in the next decade.

PATHOLOGICAL BLOOD AND BONE MARROW CELLS

Although interesting facts have been found about leukaemic cells in culture, most of the information can also be obtained by other methods. For example, in recent years chromosome studies have been made from leukaemic cells cultured *in vitro*, but similar and possibly more accurate results have been obtained by direct treatment of cells aspirated from the patient. The fact that leukaemic cells have a reduced multiplication potential is of some interest, but the studies on the maturation of such cells is of doubtful significance. Even if it does occur it does not indicate that the cells are not neoplastic. Cell culture studies are of use in the search for maturation factors which would allow leukaemic cells to be converted into normal cells, but so far no success has been reported. As a result of his studies of such cells *in vitro*, Osgood (1955 and 1957) has put forward a 'unifying concept' of the leukaemias, lymphomas and cancers, in which he postulates that cells have an inhibitory effect on one another. When mature cells are present they inhibit immature cell multiplication, but if the mature cells are removed, then multiplication occurs. Whilst of great interest, further studies are required before its full implications can be realised. Neither have cell culture studies solved the riddle as to why and how a cell becomes leukaemic. One might have expected *in vitro* studies to help in the diagnosis and classification of leukaemia; however so far they have provided little information which is not available from other sources. The claims made that cell cultures may aid in diagnosis are exaggerated. The suggestion that the isolation of polygonal cells from such material might be of use in the diagnosis of malignant metastases has been made (Berman *et al*, 1955), but similar cells have been isolated from normal tissues and cultures of marrows containing many malignant cells may not develop such cells (Woodliff, 1962). Similarly, it has been thought that the diagnosis of myelofibrosis might be assisted by cell culture (Berman *et al*, 1955) but difficulties of obtaining marrow from patients with this condition makes this approach impractical.

Aplastic anaemia can be diagnosed because cells do not migrate out of the culture (Hiraki, 1958) but this is of little value as the same information may be more readily obtained by examination of a stained film.

THE EFFECT OF PHYSIOLOGICAL AND THERAPEUTIC AGENTS ON CELL CULTURES

Studies of the effect of various agents upon cells in culture have generally suffered from a lack of reliable and sensitive quantitative methods of assessment. A few workers have claimed quantitatively reliable results but usually statistical evaluation is not given and most reported work gives semiquantitative or qualitative assessments. The physiological reagents most often added to tissue cultures of bone marrow have been those concerned in the transformation of megaloblasts to normoblasts. The results have added to our knowledge of this subject but have not given rise to outstanding advances. Of more value is the possibility of assaying erythropoietin. If a reliable reproducible technique can be developed it would be of great value as the current methods are costly and difficult. Studies of the effect of mitotic stimulants are also potentially of great importance as they may lead to an understanding of the physiological control of cellular multiplication.

Studies of the effects of drugs have been rewarding. In many cases crude parameters have been used, but recently more reliable and reproducible measurements, such as oxygen uptake, have been used with interesting results. The differences of the effect of drugs as between sensitive and resistant leukaemic cells show that it is possible to demonstrate the *in vivo* sensitivity of some cell types by *in vitro* techniques. These studies may well prove to be of interest clinically. They also provide a method of testing newly isolated or synthesised agents which might be therapeutically useful.

Culture media

Culture media are discussed on pages 5 and 6 and in Chapter 6.

They may be made from first grade chemicals and triple distilled water, or purchased from Difco, Microbiological Associates, or C.S.L.

HANKS' SOLUTION

This solution was described by Hanks and Wallace (1949). The following are the ingredients of the Difco preparation:

Sodium chloride	8·0 g
Potassium chloride	4·0 g
Calcium chloride	14·0 g
Magnesium sulphate	0·1 g
Magnesium chloride	0·1 g
Disodium phosphate	0·06 g
Monopotassium phosphate	0·06 g
Dextrose	1 g
Phenol red	0·02 g
Sodium bicarbonate	0·35 g
Triple distilled water	1,000 ml

EARLE'S SOLUTION

This solution was described by Earle (1943). The following are the ingredients of the Difco preparation:

Sodium chloride	6·8 g
Potassium chloride	0·4 g
Calcium chloride	0·2 g
Magnesium sulphate	0·2 g
Monosodium phosphate	0·125 g
Dextrose	1·0 g
Sodium bicarbonate	2·2 g
Phenol red	0·05 g

Triple distilled water 1,000 ml
The pH is adjusted to 7.4 with carbon dioxide.

KREBS' BUFFER SOLUTION
(as modified by Bisset and Alexander, 1960)

The buffer solution has the following composition:

    83 volumes 0·90 per cent (w/v) sodium chloride
    4 volumes 1·15 per cent (w/v) potassium chloride
    1 volume 2·11 per cent (w/v) anhydrous potassium
                    dihydrogen phosphate
    1 voluoe 3·82 per cent (w/v) magnesium sulphate
                    heptahydrate
    3 volumes 1·30 per cent (w/v) sodium bicarbonate
    18 volumes sodium phosphate buffer solution

    100 volumes 0·1 M disodium hydrogen phosphate.
    25 volumes 0·1 M sodium dihydrogen phosphate.

These solutions are made up and mixed together immediately before use. The pH of the medium is finally adjusted to 7.40 ± 0.05 by the addition of iso-osmotic disodium hydrogen phosphate solution containing 1.725 g/100 ml of the anhydrous salt. To each 100 ml of buffer solution used in a single experiment 100 mg glucose is added.

MEDIUM 199

This solution was described by Morgan *et al* (1950). The following are the ingredients of the Difco preparation; Hanks's salt solution is used to replace the Earle's salt solution used in the original.

l-Arginine	70 mg
l-Histidine	20 mg
l-Lysine	70 mg
l-Tyrosine	40 mg
dl-Tryptophane	20 mg
dl-Phenylalanine	50 mg
l-Cystine	20 mg
dl-Methionine	30 mg
dl-Serine	50 mg
dl-Threonine	60 mg
dl-Leucine	120 mg
dl-Isoleucine	40 mg
dl-Valine	50 mg

dl-Glutamic acid	150 mg
dl-Aspartic acid	60 mg
dl-Alanine	50 mg
l-Proline	40 mg
l-Hydroxyproline	10 mg
Glycine	50 mg
l-Cysteine	0·1 mg
Adenine	10 mg
Guanine	0·3 mg
Xanthine	0·3 mg
Hypoxanthine	0·3 mg
Thymine	0·3 mg
Uracil	0·3 mg
Thiamine	0·01 mg
Riboflavin	0·01 mg
Pyridoxine	0·025 mg
Pyridoxal	0·025 mg
Niacin	0·025 mg
Niacinamide	0·025 mg
Pantothenate	0·01 mg
Biotin	0·01 mg
Folic Acid	0·01 mg
Choline	0·5 mg
Inositol	0·05 mg
p-Aminobenzoic acid	0·05 mg
Vitamin A	0·1 mg
Calciferol	0·1 mg
Menadione	0·01 mg
a-Tocopherol phosphate	0·01 mg
Ascorbic acid	0·05 mg
Glutathione	0·05 mg
Cholesterol	0·2 mg
l-Glutamine	100 mg
Adenosinetriphosphate	1·0 mg
Adenylic acid	0·2 mg
Ribose	0·5 mg
Desoxyribose	0·5 mg
Tween 80	5·0 mg
Sodium acetate	50 mg
Iron (as Ferric nitrate)	0·1 mg

Sodium chloride	8·0 g
Potassium chloride	0·4 g
Calcium chloride	0·14 g
Magnesium sulphate	0·2 g
Disodium phosphate	0·06 g
Monopotassium phosphate	0·06 g
Sodium bicarbonate	0·35 g
Dextrose	1·0 g
Phenol red	0·02 g
Carbon dioxide	to pH 7·2
Triple distilled water	1,000 ml

EAGLE'S MEDIA

Eagle (1955) described media suitable for HeLa cells and for L cells. The following are the ingredients of the Difco preparations:

Eagle HeLa:

l-Arginine	17·4 mg
l-Cystine	12 mg
l-Histidine	7·8 mg
l-Isoleucine	26·2 mg
l-Leucine	26·2 mg
l-Lysine	29·2 mg
l-Methionine	7·5 mg
l-Phenylalanine	16·5 mg
l-Threonine	23·8 mg
l-Tryptophan	4·1 mg
l-Tyrosine	18·1 mg
l-Valine	23·4 mg
Biotin	0·24 mg
Choline chloride	0·14 mg
Choline	0·12 mg
Folic acid	0·44 mg
Pantothenate	0·48 mg
Pantothenic acid	0·22 mg
Pyridoxal	0·2 mg
Thiamine	0·34 mg
Nicotinamide	0·12 mg
Riboflavin	0·04 mg
Phenol red	5·0 mg
Dextrose	0·9 g

Sodium chloride	5·85 g
Potassium chloride	0·373 g
Calcium chloride	0·111 g
Magnesium chloride	0·102 g
Monosodium phosphate	0·138 g
Sodium bicarbonate	1·68 g
Triple distilled water	1,000 ml

Eagle L:

l-Arginine	17·4 mg
l-Cystine	4·8 mg
l-Histidine	3·1 mg
l-Isoleucine	26·2 mg
l-Leucine	13·1 mg
l-Lysine	14·6 mg
l-Methionine	7·5 mg
l-Phenylalanine	8·3 mg
l-Threonine	11·9 mg
l-Tryptophane	2·0 mg
l-Tyrosine	18·1 mg
l-Valine	11·7 mg
Biotin	0·24 mg
Choline chloride	0·14 mg
Choline	0·12 mg
Folic acid	0·44 mg
Pantothenate	0·48 mg
Pantothenic acid	0·22 mg
Pyridoxal	0·2 mg
Thiamine	0·34 mg
Nicotinamide	0·12 mg
Riboflavin	0·04 mg
Phenol red	5·0 mg
Dextrose	0·9 g
Sodium chloride	5·85 g
Potassium chloride	0·373 g
Calcium Chloride	0·111 g
Magnesium chloride	0·102 g
Monosodium phosphate	0·138 g
Sodium bicarbonate	1·68 g
Triple distilled water	1,000 ml

Addresses

Cell Culture Societies:

British Tissue Culture Association
Dr J. Paul, *Secretary/Treasurer*
Biochemistry Department
The University
Glasgow W2, Scotland

Cell Culture Society of Victoria
Mr I. Jack, *Honorary Secretary*
Tissue Culture Department
Royal Children's Hospital
Melbourne N3
Victoria, Australia

Tissue Culture Association
Duncan C. Hetherington
Duke Hospital
Durham North Carolina
United States of America

Suppliers of Media:

Difco Laboratories
Detroit 1, Michigan
United States of America

Commonwealth Serum Laboratories
Parkville N2
Victoria, Australia

Microbiological Associates
4813 Bethesda Avenue
Bethesda 14, Maryland
United States of America

References

In addition to those referred to in the text, the bibliography contains a number of additional references, marked with an asterisk, which may be of value to workers wishing to consult the original literature on this subject.

ACKERMAN, G. A. and BELLIOS, N. C. (1955a) A study of the morphology of the living cells of blood and bone marrow in vital films with the phase contrast microscope; normal blood and bone marrow. *Blood*, **10**, 3

ACKERMAN, G. A. and BELLIOS, N. C. (1955b) A study of the morphology of the living cells of blood and bone marrow in supravital films with the phase contrast microscope; blood and bone marrow from various hematologic dyscrasias. *Blood*, **10**, 1183

ALBRECHT, M. (1950) Untersuchungen über die Einwirkung von Xanthopterin auf menschliches Knockenmark *in vitro*. (Investigation on the effect of xanthopterin on human bone marrow *in vitro*). *Ärztl. Wschr.*, **5**, 878

ALBRECHT, M. (1951) Studien zur Frage der Erythroblastenentkerning an Kulturen von Meerschweinchenknockenmark. (Study on the question of the expulsion of nucleus by erythroblasts in cultures of guinea pig bone marrow). *Acta Haemat.*, **6**, 83

ALBRECHT, M. (1955) Untersuchungen über die mitosehemmende Wirkung von Demecolcin auf menschliches Knockenmark *in vitro*. (Investigations into the mitosis-inhibiting activity of demecolcine (colchicum alkaloid) on human bone marrow *in vitro*). *Acta Haemat.*, **13**, 8

ALBRECHT, M. (1957) Studien zur Thrombocytenbildung an Megakaryocyten in menschlichen Knockenmarkkulturen. (Studies of thrombocyte formation in human bone marrow culture). *Acta Haemat.*, **17**, 160

*ALBRECHT, M. (1958) Studies of the evolution of thrombocytes: experience with megakaryocytes *in vitro* (normal bone marrow and of Morbus Werlhof). *Proc. 6th Congr. Int. Soc. Haemat.*, Boston 1956, 538 (Grune and Stratton, New York)

ALBRECHT, M. and BOLL, I. (1950) Untersuchungen über die Einwirkung von Colchicin, arseniger Säure, Stickstofflost und Aethylurethan auf menschliches Knockenmark *in vitro*. (Investigations on the action of colchicine, arsenic acid, nitrogen mustards and ethyl urethan on human bone marrow *in vitro*). *Ärztl., Wschr.* **5**, 485

*ALEXANDER, W. D. and BISSET, Sheenah K. (1958) Immediate effect of triiodothyroacetic acid on oxygen consumption of myeloid leukaemic leucocytes *in vitro*. *Lancet, ii,* 1265

ALEXANDER, P. and MIKULSKI, Z. B. (1961) Differences in the response of leukaemia cells in tissue culture to nitrogen mustard and to dimethyl myleran. *Biochem. Pharmacol.* **5**, 275

ANG, Benilda, JAROSS, Lorene and MCALLISTER, R. M. (1962) Studies of fibroblast-like cells from the bone marrow of leukemic and non-leukemic children. *Proc. Soc. Exp. Biol., N.Y.,* **109**, 467

*ASTALDI, G., ALLEGRI, A. and MAURI, C. (1947) Experimental investigations of the proliferative activity of erythroblasts in their different stages of maturation. *Experientia,* **3**, 1

ASTALDI, G. and BALDINI, M. (1950) Niacynamide's effect on surviving megaloblasts *in vitro*. *Acta Haemat.,* **3**, 255

ASTALDI, G., BALDINI, M. and FRUGONI, C. Jr. (1948) Transformazione normoblasica del midollo osseo nell'anemia perniciosa ottenuta *in vitro* per azione diretta dell'estratto epatico. (Transformation of normoblastic bone marrow in pernicious anaemia obtained *in vitro* by direct action of liver extract). *Haematologica,* **31**, 265

*ASTALDI, G. and CARDINALI, G. (1957) Cytology of B_{12} deficiency *in vitro*. *Gazz. Int. Med. Chir.,* **62**, 1945

*ASTALDI, G., GALLO, V. and SALERA, U. (1951) Study on the growth of the erythroblast in normal and bone-marrow erythroblastosis conditions. *Experientia,* **7**, 280

ASTALDI, G. and MAURI, C. (1949) La valutazione dell'attivita proliferative delle cellule midollari. Studio di un *Test Statmocimetico*. (An evaluation of the proliferative activity of bone marrow studied by the *statmokinetic test*). *Haematologica,* **23**, 583

ASTALDI, G. and MAURI, C. (1950) New criteria for the evaluation of the bone-marrow cells mitotic activity. *Sang,* **21**, 378

ASTALDI, G., MAURI, C. and SALERA, U. (1950) Études *in vitro* sur la maturation et la prolifération des érythroblastes de l'anémie hypochrome essentielle. (*In vitro* studies on the maturation and proliferation of erythroblasts of essential hypochromic anaemia). *Rev. Hémat.,* **5**, 634

ASTALDI, G., MAURI, C. and SALERA, U. (1951) Richerche circa l'influenza dell'estratto embionario sulla proliferazione dell'eritroblasto del midollo osseo umano sopravivente. (Research into the influence of embryo extract on the proliferation of erythroblasts from the human bone marrow *in vitro*). *Haematologica*, **35**, 867

ASTALDI, G. and TOLENTINO, P. (1949) Studies *in vitro* on the maturation of erythroblasts in normal and pathological conditions. *J. Clin. Path.*, **2**, 217

ASTALDI, G. and TOLENTINO, P. (1952) Studies on the pathogenesis of thalassaemia. *J. Clin. Path.*, **5**, 140

ASTALDI, G., TOLENTINO, P. and SACCHETTI, C. (1951) La talassemia. (Thalassaemia). *Tipografia de Libro*, Pavia

AVROROFF, P. P. and TIMOFEEVSKY, A. D. (1914) Kultivierungsversuche von Leukämischen Blute. (Experiments in the cultivation of leukaemic blood). *Virchows Arch.*, **216**, 184

AVROROFF, P. P. and TIMOFEEVSKY, A. D. (1915) Tissue cultures of blood and blood-forming tissues. Quoted by BLOOM, W. (1938) in Downey's *Handbook of Haematology* (Hoeber, New York)

BAIKIE, A. G., COURT-BROWN, W. M., BUCKTON, K. E., HARNDEN, D. G., JACOBS, P. A. and TOUGH, I. M. (1960) A possible specific chromosome abnormality in human chronic myeloid leukaemia. *Nature*, **188**, 1165

BALDINI, M. and SACCHETTI, C. (1953) L'effet de la cystine et de la cystéine sur la moelle osseuse humaine, cultivée en milieu carencé en amino-acides. (The effect of cystine and cysteine on human bone marrow cultured in a medium deficient in amino acids). *Rev. Hémat.*, **8**, 3

*BALL, W. D. and AUERBACH, R. (1960) *In vitro* formation of lymphocytes from embryonic thymus. *Exp. Cell Res.*, **20**, 245

BANGA, I. and BALO, J. (1953) Elastin and elastase. *Nature*, **171**, 44

BANNERMAN, R. M. (1961) Thalassemia. A survey of some aspects. (Grune and Stratton, New York and London)

BANNERMAN, R. M., GRINSTEIN, M. and MOORE, C. V. (1959) Haemoglobin synthesis in thalassaemia; *in vitro* studies. *Brit. J. Haemat.*, **5**, 102

*BARNARDELLI, E., MELE, V. and GORINI, P. (1952) Richerche sull'attivita proliferativa e differenziativa dell'erithroblasto della pollicitemia vera. (Research on the proliferative activity and differentiation of erythroblasts in polycythaemia vera). *Haematologica*, **36**, 891

*BENDER, M. A. and PRESCOTT, D. M. (1962) DNA synthesis and mitosis in cultures of human peripheral leukocytes. *Exp. Cell Res.*, **27**, 221

BENEVOLENSKAYA, S. V. (1930) Haematopoiesis in cultures of the embryonic liver of man. *Arch. exp. Zellforsch.*, **9**, 128

BERG, R. B. and ROSENTHAL, M. S. (1961) Studies of fibroblastic cells cultivated from bone marrow of leukemic and non-leukemic patients. *Proc. Soc. Exp. Biol.*, **106**, 614

BERMAN, L. and POWSNER, E. R. (1959) Review of methods for studying maturation of human erythroblasts *in vitro*: evaluation of a new method of culture of cell suspension in a clot-free medium. *Blood*, **14**, 1194

BERMAN, L. and STULBERG, C. S. (1956) Eight culture strains (Detroit) of human epithelial-like cells. *Proc. Soc. Exp. Biol.*, **92**, 730

BERMAN, L., STULBERG, C. S. and RUDDLE, F. H. (1955) Long-term tissue culture of human bone marrow. I. Report of isolation of a strain of cells resembling epithelial cells from bone marrow of a patient with carcinoma of the lung. *Blood*, **10**, 896

BERMAN, L., STULBERG, C. S. and RUDDLE, F. H. (1956) Epithelium-like cells derived from tissue cultures of human bone marrow and ascitic fluid. *J. Mich. Med. Soc.*, **55**, 269

BERMAN, L., STULBERG, C. S. and RUDDLE, F. H. (1957a) Criteria of malignancy; morphology of Detroit strains of human cells in tissue culture. *Trans. N.Y. Acad. Sci.*, **19**, 432

BERMAN, L., STULBERG, C. S. and RUDDLE, F. H. (1957b) Human cell culture. Morphology of the Detroit strains. *Cancer Res.*, **17**, 668

*BERMANN, G. (1925) Über die Infektion von Knockenmarkskulturen jugendlicher und ausgewachsener Meerschweinchen mit *Staphylococcus pyogenes aureus*. (On the infection of bone marrow cultures of young and adult guinea pigs with *Staphylococcus pyogenes aureus*). *Arch. exp. Zellforsch.*, **1**, 392

*BERNARDELLI, E., RONDANELLI, E. G. and GORINI, P. (1952) Ricerca sull'attivita proliferativa e differenziativa dell'eritroblasto della policitemia vera. (Research on the proliferative activity and differentiation of erythroblasts in polycythaemia vera). *Haematologica*, **36**, 891

BIANCHINI, E. and SACCHETTI, C. (1955) Il comportamento isto-chimico dei polisaccaridi e dei lipidi nei megacariociti normali e patologici coltivati *in vitro*. (The histochemical behaviour of polysaccharides and lipids in normal and pathological megakaryocytes cultured *in vitro*). *Haematologica*, **40**, 53

*BICHEL, J. (1938) Dauerzüchtung von leukämischen Zellen *in vitro*. (Continuous growth of leukaemic cells *in vitro*). *Ztschr. Krebsforsch.*, **48**, 92

BICHEL, J. (1939)　On the cultivation of a mouse leukosis *in vitro*. (University Press of Aarhus).

*BICHEL, J. (1940)　Über eine Technik zur Züchtung leukotischer Zellen *in vitro*, sowie einige Bemerkungen über die Pathogenese der Leukosen. (On a technique for the growth of leukaemic cells *in vitro*, some remarks on the pathogenesis of leukaemia). *Arch. exp. Zellforsch.*, **24**, 27

BICHEL, J. (1952)　Cultivation of leukemic cells in tissue culture. *Acta Path. Microbiol. Scand.*, **31**, 410

BICZ, W. (1960)　The influence of carbon dioxide tension on the respiration of normal and leukemic human leukocytes. I. Influence on endogenous respiration. *Cancer Res.*, **20**, 184

BIESELE, J. J. (1954a)　Assay of carcinolytic and carcinostatic agents. *Ann. N.Y. Acad. Sci.*, **58**, 1129

BIESELE, J. J. (1954b)　Effects of 6-mercaptopurine on experimental tumors in tissue culture. *Ann. N.Y. Acad. Sci.*, **60**, 228

BIESELE, J. J. (1955)　Antagonistic effects of 6-mercaptopurine and co-enzyme A on mitochondria and mitosis in tissue culture. *J. Biophys. Biochem. Cytol.*, **1**, 119

BIESELE, J. J. (1956)　Tissue culture and cancer. *Sci. Amer.*, **195**, 50

BIESELE, J. J. (1958)　Tumor-specific cytotoxicity of anti-tumor agents. *Ann. N.Y. Acad. Sci.*, **76**, 530

BIESELE, J. J. and BERGER, Ruth E. (1950)　The effect of xanthopterin and related agents on the proliferation of rabbit marrow cells *in vitro*. *Cancer Res.*, **10**, 686

BIESELE, J. J., SLAUTTERBACK, Marilyn C. and MARGOLIS, Marilyn (1955)　Unsubstituted purine and its riboside as toxic antimetabolites in mouse tissue cultures. *Cancer*, **8**, 87

BIGGS, Rosemary (1951)　The reliability of some haematological measurements. In *Recent Advances in Clinical Pathology* (Churchill, London), p. 318

BILLEN, D. (1957)　Recovery of lethally irradiated mice by treatment with bone marrow cells maintained *in vitro*. *Nature*, **179**, 574

BILLEN, D. (1959)　The potentialities of tissue cultured cells of hemic origin in X-irradiated mice. *Radiation Biology and Cancer* (University of Texas Press, Austin), p. 223

*BILLEN, D. (1959)　Effect of bone marrow culture in *vitro* on its protective action in irradiated mice. *J. Nat. Cancer Inst.*, **23**, 1389

*BILLEN, D. and DEBRUNNER, G. A. (1960)　Continuously propagating cells derived from normal mouse bone marrow. *J. Nat. Cancer Inst.*, **25**, 1127

BISCEGLIE, V. (1929)　Cultura *in vitro* di sangue: le capacita evolutive dei monociti e dei linfociti. (*In vitro* culture of blood: the evolution of monocytes and lymphocytes). *Boll. Sci. Med.*, **101**, 393

BISSET, Sheenah K. and ALEXANDER, W. D. (1960) The effect of metabolic stimulants on the oxygen uptake of normal and leukaemic human leucocytes *in vitro*. *Quart. J. Exp. Physiol.*, **45**, 18

BLACKBURN, E. K. and LAJTHA, L. G. (1951) Erythroleukemia. *Blood*, **6**, 261

BLACKBURN, E. K. and LAJTHA, L. G. (1954) The deficiency theory of blast cell leukaemias. *J. Clin. Path.*, **7**, 168

BLOOM, W. (1927) Transformation of lymphocytes of thoracic duct into polyblasts (macrophages) in tissue culture. *Proc. Soc. Exp. Biol.*, **24**, 567

BLOOM, W. (1938) Tissue cultures of blood and blood-forming tissues; Downey's *Handbook of Hematology* (Hoeber, New York, 1938), **2**, 1469

*BOND, V. P., FLIEDNER, T. M., CRONKITE, E. P., RUBINI, J. R., BRECHER, G. and SCHORK, P. K. (1959) Proliferative potentials of bone marrow and blood cells studied by *in vitro* uptake of H3-thymidine. *Acta Haemat.*, **21**, 1

*BORSOOK, H., DEASY, Clara L., HAAGEN-SMIT, A. J., KEIGHLEY, G. and LOWY, P. H. (1952) Incorporation *in vitro* of labelled amino acids into proteins of rabbit reticulocytes. *J. Biol. Chem.*, **196**, 669

BREBNER, H., BOTTOMLEY, A. C. and WILKINSON, J. F. (1954) Biochemical changes in cultured cells. *Nature*, **174**, 1196

BROOKE, J. H. (1959) Personal communication

BROOKE, J. H., MCNEESE, J. and OSGOOD, E. E. (1958) The gradient tissue culture method as an aid in classification of acute leukemias. *Proc. 6th Congr. Int. Soc. Haemat.*, *Boston* 1956, (Grune and Stratton, New York), p. 238

BROOKE, J. H. and OSGOOD, E. E. (1959) Long-term mixed cultures of human hemic cells, with granulocytic, lymphocytic, plasmocytic and erythrocytic series represented. *Blood*, **14**, 803

BUCHSBAUM, R. and KUNTZ, J. A. (1954) The effects of certain stimulants and depressants on individual fibroblasts in a perfusion chamber. *Ann. N.Y. Acad. Sci.*, **58**, 1303

BURCHENAL, J. H., MURPHY, M. L., ELISON, R. R., SYKES, M. P., TAN, T. C., LEONE, L. A., KARNOFSKY, D. A., CRAVER, L. F., DARGEON, H. W. and RHOADS, C. P. (1953) Clinical evaluation of a new antimetabolite, 6-mercaptopurine, in the treatment of leukemia and allied diseases. *Blood*, **8**, 966

*BURK, D., LASZLO, J., HUNTER, J., KENT, W. and WOOD, M. (1960) Differential metabolic responses of susceptible and resistant mouse leukemia cells to 8–azaguanine. *J. Nat. Cancer Inst.*, **24**, 57

BURROWS, M. T. (1910) The cultivation of tissues of the chick embryo outside the body. *J. Amer. Med. Ass.*, **55**, 2057

*BURROWS, M. T. (1912) A method of furnishing a continuous supply of new medium to a tissue culture *in vitro*. *Anat. Rec.*, **6**, 141

*BUSSI, L., POZZA, G., ERIDANI, S., FAVA, P. L. and DE MICHELI, E. (1955) Investigazione *in vitro* sul comportamento del tissuto megaloblastico nella presenza di vari fattori capace d'influire sui processi di maturazione cellulare. (Investigations on the behaviour *in vitro* of the megaloblastic tissue in the presence of different factors acting upon the processes of cellular maturation). *Recentia Med.* (*Roma*), **20**, 109

CAFFIER, P. (1927)   Über die Umwandlungsfähigkeit der weissen Elemente des normalen menschlichen Blutes bei *in vitro*-Kultwierung. (On the capacity for transformation of the white elements of normal human blood in *in vitro* cultures). *Arch. exp. Zellforsch.*, **4**, 419

CAFFIER, P. (1928) Die prospektive Portenzen des normalen Menschenblutes. (The prospective potentialities of normal human blood). *Arch. exp. Zellforsch.*, **6**, 285

*CAILLEAU, Relda and KIRK, P. L. (1957) Some factors affecting the growth-promoting properties of serum in tissue culture. *Texas Rep. Biol. Med.*, **15**, 237

CAIRNS, H. J. F. and LAJTHA, L. G. (1948)   Loss of white cells in bone marrow culture. *Nature*, **162**, 536

CALLENDER, Sheila T. and LAJTHA, L. C. (1951)   The effect of citrovorum factor (folinic acid) on megaloblasts *in vitro*. *J. Clin. Path.*, **4**, 204

*CALLENDER, Sheila T. and LAJTHA, L. C. (1951) On the nature of Castle's hemopoietic factor. *Blood*, **6**, 1234

*CARDINALI, G., CARDINALI, Giuliana and BLAIR, J. (1962) The statmokinetic effect of vincaleukoblastine on normal bone marrow and leukemic cells. *Cancer Res.*, **21**, 1542

*CARREL, A. (1912) On the permanent life of tissues outside of the organism. *J. Exp. Med.*, **15**, 516

CARREL, A. (1913) Artificial activation of the growth *in vitro* of connective tissue. *J. Exp. Med.*, **17**, 14

CARREL, A. (1923) A method for the physiological study of tissues *in vitro*. *J. Exp. Med.*, **38**, 407

*CARREL, A. (1931) Maintien de la constance du milieu dans les cultures de tissus. (Maintenance of constancy of the medium in tissue culture). *C.R. Soc. Biol.*, **106**, 7

*CARREL, A. (1934)   Monocytes as an indicator of certain states of blood serum. *Science*, **80**, 565

CARREL, A. and BURROWS, M. T. (1910a) Cultivation of sarcoma outside of the body. A second note. *J. Amer. Med. Ass.*, **54**, 1554

CARREL, A. and BURROWS, M. T. (1910b) Culture de substance rénale en dehors de l'organisme (Deuxiéme note). (Culture of kidney *in vitro*. Second note). *C.R. Soc. Biol.*, **69**, 298

CARREL, A. and BURROWS, M. T. (1910c) Cultivation of adult tissues and organs outside the body. *J. Amer. Med. Ass.*, **55**, 1379

CARREL, A. and BURROWS, M. T. (1910d) Culture de moelle osseuse et de rate (Troisième note). (Bone marrow and spleen culture. Third note). *C.R. Soc. Biol.*, **69**, 299

CARREL, A. and EBELING, A. H. (1922) Pure cultures of large mononuclear leucocytes. *J. Exp. Med.*, **36**, 365

CARREL, A. and EBELING, A. H. (1926a) The transformation of monocytes into fibroblasts through the action of Rous virus. *J. Exp. Med.*, **43**, 461

*CARREL, A. and EBELING, A. H. (1926b) The fundamental properties of the fibroblast and the macrophage. *J. Exp. Med.*, **44**, 285

*CATER, D. B., PHILLIPS, A. F. and SILVER, I. A. (1956) The measurement of oxidation-reduction potentials and oxygen tension as a tool for the investigation of chemotherapeutic drugs *in vivo*. *G. Ital. Chimioter.*, **3**, 3

CATER, D. B., PHILLIPS, A. F. and SILVER, I. A. (1957) Apparatus and techniques for the measurement of oxidation-reduction potentials, pH and oxygen tension *in vivo*. *Proc. Roy. Soc. Biol.*, **146**, 289

CATER, D. B., SILVER, I. A. and WILSON, G. M. (1959) Apparatus and technique for the quantitative measurement of oxygen tension in living tissues. *Proc. Roy. Soc. Biol.*, **151**, 256

CHANG, R. S. (1960) Genetic study of human cells *in vitro*. Carbohydrate variants from cultures of HeLa and conjunctival cells. *J. Exp. Med.*, **111**, 235

*CHANG, R. S. (1961) A comparative study of the growth, nutrition and metabolism of the primary and the transformed human cells *in vitro*. *J. Exp. Med.*, **113**, 405

*CHANG, R. S., PENNELL, R. B., KELLER, W., WHEATON, L. and LIEPENS, Helen (1959) Macromolecular growth requirements of human cells in continuous culture. *Proc. Soc. Exp., Biol.*, **102**, 213

CHEN, J. M. (1954) The cultivation in fluid medium of organised liver pancreas and other tissues of foetal rats. *Exp. Cell Res.*, **7**, 518

*CLEMMESEN, J., ESPERSON, T. and PLUM, C. M. (1948) *In vitro* study of bone marrow. III. Erythropoiesis *in vitro* of sternal marrow from cases of pernicious anaemia and lymphatic leukosis under therapy. *Blood*, **3**, 155

CLEMMESEN, J. and PLUM, C. M. (1952) A simplified method for *in vitro* examination of the erythropoiesis of bone marrow applied to cases of pernicious anemia and leukosis. *Acta Physiol. Scand.*, **25,** 188

COOPER, E. H., BARKHAM, P. and HALE, A. J. (1961)   Mitogenic activity of phytohemagglutinin. *Lancet, ii,* 210

CRADDOCK, C. G. and NAKAI, G. S. (1962) Leukemic cell proliferation as determined by *in vitro* deoxyribonucleic acid synthesis. *J. Clin. Invest.*, **41,** 360

CRAVEN, C. (1958) Personal communication

DANES, B. S. (1957) Suspension cultures of strain L mouse fibroblasts. I. A glass stirrer apparatus for the cultivation of cell suspensions. *Exp. Cell Res.*, **12,** 169

*DANES, B. S. and KIELER, J. (1958)   The influence of CO_2 tension on cellular respiration studied by the Cartesian diver technique. *C.R. Lab. Carlsberg*, **31,** 61

DANNEEL, H. (1897) Über den durch diffundierende Gase hervorrufenen Reststrom. (On the produced residual current through diffusing gases). *Z. Elektrochemie,* **4,** 227

DAVIES, P. W. and BRINK, F. Jr. (1942) Microelectrodes for measuring oxygen tension in animal tissues. *Rev. Sci. Instrum.*, **13,** 524

DAVIS, J. G. M. and WOODLIFF, H. J.   (1960)   Oxygen   tension measurements in bone marrow fleck cultures. *Blood,* **15,** 534

*DAVIS, M. and SMITH, C. L. (1957)   The irradiation of individual parts of single cells in tissue culture with a microbeam of α particles. *Exp. Cell Res.*, **12,** 15

*DAWE, C. J. and POTTER, M. (1957)   Morphologic and biologic progression of a lymphoid neoplasm of the mouse *in vivo* and *in vitro*. *Amer. J. Path.*, **33,** 603

*DAWE, C. J., POTTER, M. and LEIGHTON, J. (1958)   Progressions of a reticulum cell sarcoma of the mouse *in vivo* and *in vitro*. *J. Nat. Cancer Inst.*, **21,** 753

*DE BRION, G. (1956) La culture des tissus leucémiques. (Culture of leukaemic tissue). *Rev. Hémat.*, **11,** 437

DE BRUYN, P. P. H. (1944)   Locomotion of blood cells in tissue culture. *Anat. Rec.*, **89,** 43

*DE BRUYN, P. P. H. (1945) The motion of the migrating cells in tissue cultures of lymph nodes. *Anat. Rec.*, **93,** 295

DE BRUYN, W. M. (1949a) *In vitro* cultivation of malignant lymphoblasts of transplantable mouse lymphosarcoma MB (T86157) without typical mesenchyme cells. *Bijdr. Dierk.*, **28,** 77

*DE BRUYN, W. M. (1949b) A study *in vitro* of a strain of lymphoblast-like cells, MB13, derived from mouse lymphosarcoma MB (T86157). *Cancer Res.*, **9**, 593

*DE BRUYN, W. M. (1949c) A study of two transplantable round cell sarcomas of the mouse T9094 (MA) and T86157 (MB) *in vivo* and *in vitro*. *Acta Un. Int. Cancer*, **6**, 621

*DE BRUYN, W. M. (1955) Het Kweken Van Leucaemische cellen en van carcinomen in Kolven. (The maintenance of leukaemic cells and carcinoma cells in continuous culture). *5e Jaarboek van Kankeronderzoek en Kankerbestrijding in Nederland*

*DE BRUYN, W. M. (1959) Some methods of and results obtained with the cultivation of blood-forming tissues and of round cell sarcomas of mice. *Haemat. Lat. (Milano)*, **2**, fasc. 10

*DE BRUYŃ, W. M. (1961) Respiration and glycolysis of the cells of cell-strain MB III! and MB VIa (transplantable mouse lymphosarcoma MB (T86157) in tissue culture under various conditions). *Path. Biol.*, **9**, 569

*DE BRUYN, W. M. and GEY, G. O. (1952) Further studies *in vitro* of transplantable mouse lymphosarcoma T86157. *Acta Un. Int. Cancer*, **7**, 772

DE BRUYN, W. M., KORTEWEG, R. and VAN WAVEREN, E. K. (1949) Transplantable mouse lymphosarcoma T86157 (BM) studied *in vivo*, *in vitro* and at autopsy. *Cancer Res.*, **9**, 282

DE HAAN, J. (1928) Das Auftreten der verschiedenen Zelltypen in Blut und Bindegewebe (Eigenschaften und Entstehungsbedingungen) nach Untersuchungen mittels der Durchstromungskultur *in vitro*. (Occurrence of various cell types in blood and connective tissues (characteristics and conditions of formation) according to investigations by means of perfusion culture *in vitro*). *Arch. exp. Zellforsch.*, **7**, 298

DE LA CHAPELLE, A. (1961) Factor stimulating cell division in cultured leucocytes. *Lancet*, *ii*, 1348

*DICK, D. A. T. (1955) An easily made tissue culture perfusion chamber. *Qu. J. Micr. Sci.*, **96**, 363

DIFCO Laboratories (1961) Commercial literature.

DOUGHERTY, I. F. and WHITE, A. (1943) Effects of pituitary adrenotrophic hormone on lymphoid tissue. *Proc. Soc. Exp. Biol.*, **53**, 132

*DRAPER, G., RAMSEY, H. J. and DUPERTUIS, C. W. (1944) Variation in behaviour of buffy coat cultures of different constitution types. *J. Clin. Invest.*, **23**, 864

EAGLE, H. (1955a) The specific amino acid requirements of a mammalian cell (strain L) in tissue culture. *J. Biol. Chem.*, **214**, 839

EAGLE, H. (1955b)   Nutritional needs of mammalian cells in tissue culture. *Science*, **122**, 501

*EAGLE, H. (1955c)   The specific amino acid requirements of a human carcinoma cell (strain HeLa) in tissue culture. *J. Exp. Med.*, **102**, 34

*EAGLE, H. (1955d)   The minimum vitamin requirements of the L and HeLa cells in tissue culture, the production of specific vitamin deficiencies and their cure. *J. Exp. Med.*, **102**, 595

*EAGLE, H. (1956)   Relative growth-promoting activity in tissue culture of co-factors and the parent vitamins. *Proc. Soc. Exp. Biol.*, **91**, 358

EAGLE, H. and FOLEY, G. E. (1956)   The cytotoxic action of carcinolytic agents in tissue culture. *Amer. J. Med.*, **21**, 739

EAGLE, H. and FOLEY, G. E. (1958)   Susceptibility of cultured human cells to anti-tumor agents. *Ann. N.Y. Acad. Sci.*, **76**, 534

EARLE, W. R. (1943)   Production of malignancy *in vitro*. IV. The mouse fibroblast cultures and changes seen in the living cells. *J. Nat. Cancer Inst.*, **4**, 165

EARLE, W. R. (1951)   Method for growth of cells on perforated cellophane. *Meth. Med. Res.*, **4**, 218

EARLE, W. R., BRYANT, J. C., SCHILLING, E. L. and EVANS, V. J. (1956)   Growth of cell suspensions in tissue culture. *Ann. N.Y. Acad. Sci.*, **63**, 666

EARLE, W. R. and HIGHHOUSE, F. (1954)   Culture flasks for use with plane surface substrate tissue cultures. *J. Nat. Cancer Inst.*, **14**, 841

EARLE, W. R., SCHILLING, E. L., BRYANT, J. C., and EVANS, V. J. (1954)   The growth of pure strain L cells in fluid-suspension cultures. *J. Nat. Cancer Inst.*, **14**, 1159

EBELING, A. H. (1921a)   Fibrin and serum as a culture medium. *J. Exp. Med.*, **33**, 641

EBELING, A. H. (1921b)   Measurement of the growth of tissues *in vitro*. *J. Exp. Med.*, **34**, 231

EDWARD, H., REISNER, E. H. and ODOM, R. (1959)   Tissue culture of bone marrow. *Haemat. Lat. (Milano)*, **2**, 91

EHRMANN, R. L. and GEY, G. O. (1953)   The use of cell colonies on glass for evaluating nutrition and growth in roller-tube cultures. *J. Nat. Cancer Inst.*, **13**, 1099

ELION, G. B., BURG, E. and HITCHINGS, G. H. (1952)   Studies on condensed pyrimidine systems. IX. The synthesis of some six substituted purines. *J. Amer. Chem. Soc.*, **74**, 411

ERDMANN, Rhoda (1917a)   Some observations concerning chicken bone marrow in plasma medium. *Proc. Soc. Exp. Biol.*, **14**, 109

ERDMANN, Rhoda (1917b)   Cytological observations on the behaviour of chicken bone marrow in plasma medium. *Amer. J. Anat.*, **22**, 73

*EVANS, V. J., BRYANT, T. C., FIORAMONTI, M. C., MCQUILKIN, W. T., SANFORD, K. K. and EARLE, W. R. (1956) Studies on nutrient media for tissue cells *in vitro*. I. A protein-free chemically defined medium for cultivation of strain L cells. *Cancer Res.*, **16**, 77

EVANS, V. J. and EARLE, W. R. (1947) The use of perforated cellophane for the growth of cells in tissue culture. *J. Nat. Cancer Inst.*, **8**, 103

EVANS, V. J., EARLE, W. R., SANFORD, K. K., SHANNON, J. E. and WALTZ, H. K. (1951) The preparation and handling of replicate tissue cultures for quantitative studies. *J. Nat. Cancer Inst.*, **11**, 907

FARBER, S., DIAMOND, L. K., MERCER, R. D., SYLVESTER, R. F. Jr. and WOLFF, J. A. (1948) Temporary remissions in acute leukemia in children produced by folic acid antagonist 4-aminopteroyl–glutamic acid (aminopterin). *New Engl. J. Med.*, **238**, 787

FARNES, Patricia and TROBAUGH, F. E. (1961a) The inhibitory effect of collagenase on bone marrow fibroblasts *in vitro*. *Exp. Cell Res.*, **24**, 612

FARNES, Patricia and TROBAUGH, F. E. (1961b) Observations on leukemic marrow explants in well cultures. *J. Lab. Clin. Med.*, **57**, 568

FEINMANN, E. L., SHARP, J. and WILKINSON, J. F. (1952) Observations on the behaviour of erythroblasts cultured in normal and 'Pernicious anaemia' sera. *Brit. Med. J.*, ii, 14

FELL, Honor B. (1951) Techniques of bone cultivation. *Meth. Med. Res.*, **4**, 234

*FELL, Honor B. (1953) Recent advances in organ culture. *Sci. Progr. No.* 162, 212

FERGUSON-SMITH, M. A. JOHNSTON, A. W. and WEINBERG, A. (1960) The chromosome complement in true hermaphroditism. *Lancet*, ii, 126

*FIESCHI, A. (1950) Sintesi dei risultati di cultura *in vivo* e *in vitro* del midollo osseo normale e patologico. (Review of results of culture *in vivo* and *in vitro* of normal and pathological bone marrow). *Ann. Inst. Med. Trop., Lisboa*, **7**, 203

FIESCHI, A. and ASTALDI, G. (1945) Il midollo osseo dell'anemia perniciosa nella cultura *in vitro*. (The bone marrow of pernicious anaemia in *in vitro* culture). *Gastroenterologia, Basel*, **70**, 171

FIESCHI, A. and ASTALDI, G. (1946a) La cultura *in vitro* del midollo osseo. (*In vitro* culture of bone marrow). *Tipografia del Libro, Pavia*

*FIESCHI, A. and ASTALDI, G. (1946b) La cultura *in vitro* del midollo osseo di leucemia emocitoblastica acuta. (The *in vitro* culture of bone marrow from acute haemocytoblastic leukaemia). *Bol. Soc. Ital. Biol. Sper.*, **22,** 485

FIESCHI, A., BIANCHINI, E., CAMBIAGGI, G., SACCHETTI, C. and SALVIDIO, E. (1956) Studies on the biological behaviour of the cells of acute leukaemia. *Acta Haemat.*, **16,** 126

FIESCHI, A., CAMBIAGGI, G. and SACCHETTI, C. (1954) Evaluation de processus leucémique aigus par la culture *in vitro* et *in vivo* de la moelle osseuse. (Evaluation of acute leukaemic processes by the *in vitro* and *in vivo* culture of bone marrow). *Sang*, **25,** 97

FIESCHI, A. and SACCHETTI, C. (1959) Dynamic behaviour of bone marrow granuloblasts in leucopenia and leucocytosis. *Acta Haemat.*, **22,** 79

FIESCHI, A. and SACCHETTI, C. (1960) The clinical applications of *in vitro* culture of bone marrow. *Panminerva Med.*, **2,** 484

FISCHER, A. (1925) Sur la transformation *in vitro* des gros leucocytes mononucléaires en fibroblastes. (Transformation *in vitro* of organism of mononuclears into fibroblasts). *C.R. Soc. Biol.*, **92,** 109

FISCHER, G. A. (1957) Tissue culture of mouse leukemic cells. *Proc. Amer. Ass. Cancer Res.*, **2,** 201

FISCHER, G. A. (1958) Studies of the culture of leukemic cells *in vitro*. *Ann. N.Y. Acad. Sci.*, **76,** 673

*FISCHER, G. A. (1959) Nutritional and amethopterin-resistant characteristics of leukemic clones. *Cancer Res.*, **19,** 372

*FISCHER, G. A. (1961) Increased levels of folic acid reductase as a mechanism of resistance to amethopterin in leukemic cells. *Biochem. Pharmacol.*, **7,** 75

*FISCHER, G. A. and WELCH, A. D. (1957) Effect of citrovorum factor and peptones on mouse leukemia cells L5178 in tissue culture. *Science*, **126,** 1018

*FISCHER, H. W. and PUCK, T. T. (1956) On the functions of x-irradiated *feeder* cells in supporting growth of single mammalian cells. *Proc. Nat. Acad. Sci., Washington*, **42,** 900

*FOLEY, G. E., FRIEDMAN, O. M. and DROLET, B. P. (1961) Studies on the mechanism of action of cytoxan. Evidence of activation *in vivo* and *in vitro*. *Cancer Res.*, **21,** 57

FOOT, N. C. (1912) Über das Wachsturn von Knockenmark *in vitro*. Experimenteller Beitrag zur Entstehung des Fettyewekes. (The growth of bone marrow *in vitro*. Experimental contribution to the development of fatty tissue). *Beitr. Path. Anat.*, **53,** 446

FOOT, N. C. (1913) The growth of chicken bone marrow *in vitro* and its bearing on haematogenesis in adult life. *J. Exp. Med.*, **17,** 43

FORD, C. E., JACOBS, P. A. and LAJTHA, L. G. (1958) Human somatic chromosomes. *Nature*, **181**, 1565

FRANCO, J. and ARKUN, S. N. (1951) Action de l'acidie 4–aminoptéroyl glutamique (aminopterin) *in vitro* sur une culture de moelle d'anémie pernicieuse. (The effect of 4–amino–pteroylglutamic acid (aminopterin) *in vitro* on a culture of pernicious anaemia marrow). *Sang*, **22**, 413

FUJITA, S. and TAKINO, T. (1960) Analysis of culture patterns of normal and leukaemic bone marrows. *Exp. Cell Res.*, **20**, 262

GAVOSTO, F., MARAINI, G. and PILERI, A. (1960) Proliferative capacity of acute leukaemia cells. *Nature*, **187**, 611

*GAVOSTO, F., MARAINI, G. and PILERI, A. (1960) Nucleic acids and protein metabolism in acute leukemia cells. *Blood*, **16**, 1555

GEMMILL, C. L., GEY, G. O. and AUSTRIAN, R. (1940) The metabolism of tissue cultures of Walker rat sarcoma 319. *Bull. Johns Hopk. Hosp.*, **66**, 167

GEY, G. O. (1933) An improved technic for massive cell culture. *Amer. J. Cancer*, **17**, 752

GEY, G. O. (1949) Bulletin of the Tissue Culture Association, **3**, 16. Quoted by STEWART, D. C. and KIRK, P. L. (1954), *Biol. Rev.*, **29**, 119

*GINSBURG, H. and SACHS, L. (1961) Long-term cultivation in tissue culture of leukemic cells from mouse leukemia induced by Moloney virus or by X rays. *J. Nat. Cancer Inst.*, **27**, 1153

GOLDSTEIN, M. N. and MCCORMICK T. M. (1957) Cytochemical studies during the differentiation of normal human monocytes *in vitro*. *Amer. J. Path.*, **33**, 737

GORDON, A. S. (1960) Humoral influences on blood cell formation and release. Ciba Foundation Symposium. *Haemopoiesis. Cell production and its regulation* (Churchill, London), p. 362

GROSSMAN, W. (1924) Über Knockenmark *in vitro*. (Bone marrow *in vitro*). *Beitr. path. Anat.*, **72**, 195

GUNZ, F. W. (1948a) Culture of human leukaemic blood cells *in vitro*: technique and the growth curve. *Brit. J. Cancer*, **2**, 29

GUNZ, F. W. (1948b) Culture of human leukaemic blood cells *in vitro*: normal and abnormal cell division and maturation. *Brit. J. Cancer*, **2**, 41

GUNZ, F. W. (1949) Studies of leukaemic blood *in vitro* with special reference to the effect of some therapeutic agents. *Ph.D. Thesis*, Cambridge University

I

GUNZ, F. W. (1950) The effect of 4–amino–pteroylglutamic acid (aminopterin) on human leukemic leukocytes *in vitro*. *Blood*, **5**, 161

HAAGEN, E. (1927) Die Bedentung der Ionen im Kulturmedium für die explantierte Zelle. (The significance of ions in culture medium for the explant cell). *Arch. exp. Zellforsch.*, **3**, 353

HALEY, E. E., FISCHER, G. A. and WELCH, A. D. (1961) The requirements for L–asparagine of mouse leukemia cells L5178Y in culture. *Cancer Res.*, **21**, 532

HANKS, J. H. (1948) The longevity of chick tissue cultures without renewal of medium. *J. Cell Comp. Physiol.*, **31**, 235

HANKS, J. H. and WALLACE Roslyn, E. (1949) Relation of oxygen and temperature in the preservation of tissues by refrigeration. *Proc. Soc. Exp. Biol.*, **71**, 196

*HARRIS, H. (1955) Some quantitative studies of the multiplication of connective tissue cells *in vitro*. *Brit. J. Exp. Path.*, **36**, 115

*HARRIS, H. (1955) The sulphur requirements of rat connective tissue cells. *Brit. J. Exp. Path.*, **36**, 454

HARRIS, H. (1956) The relationship between the respiration and multiplication of rat connective tissue cells *in vitro*. *Brit. J. Exp. Path.*, **37**, 512

HARRIS, H. and BARCLAY, W. R. (1955) A method for measuring the respiration of animal cells *in vitro* with some observations on the macrophages of the rabbit. *Brit. J. Exp. Path.*, **36**, 592

*HARRISON, K. and RANDAL, F. W. (1948) An application of bone marrow culture to toxicology and therapeutics. *Quart. J. Exp. Physiol.*, **34**, 141

HARRISON, R. G. (1907) Observations on living developing nerve fibre. *Proc. Soc. Exp. Biol.*, **4**, 140

*HARRISON, R. G. (1910) The outgrowth of the nerve fibre as a mode of protoplasmic movement. *J. Exp. Zool.*, **9**, 787

*HASTINGS, J., FREEDMAN, S., RENDON, O., COOPER, H. L. and HIRSCHHORN, K. (1961) Culture of human white cells using differential leucocyte separation. *Nature*, **192**, 1214

HAYHOE, F. G. J. (1960) Leukaemia. Research and clinical practice. (Churchill, London) p. 74

*HAYS, E. E. (1946) Effect of folic acid upon primitive erythrocytes *in vitro*. *Proc. Soc. Exp. Biol.*, **63**, 558

HEALY, G. M., FISHER, D. C. and PARKER, R. C. (1955) Nutrition of animal cells in tissue culture. *Proc. Soc. Exp. Biol.*, **89**, 71

*HERZENBERG, L. A. and ROOSA, R. A. (1960) Nutritional requirements for growth of a mouse lymphoma in cell culture. *Exp. Cell Res.*, **21**, 430

*HIRAKI, K. (1956) Diagnosis of leukaemia and aplastic anaemia by bone marrow culture. *Acta Med. Okayama*, **10**, 130

HIRAKI, K. (1958a) The function of the megakaryocyte (motility, separation of the platelet and phagocytosis): observations both in idiopathic thrombocytopenic purpura and in normal adults. *Proc. 6th Congr. Int. Soc. Haemat.*, *Boston 1956* (Grune and Stratton, New York), p. 537

HIRAKI, K. (1958b) Studies on diagnosis of leukemia by tissue culture. *Acta Med. Okayama*, **12**, 84

HIRAKI, K. (1961) Personal communication

*HIRAKI, K., FRINO, S. and SOTA, S. (1962) Studies on chemotherapy of leukemia by a new bone-marrow tissue culture technic. *Proc. 8th Congr. Int. Dox. Haemat.*, *Vienna 1961* (Karger, Basle/ New York), p. 347

*HIRAKI, K. and OFUJI, T. (1956) Microcinematographic observations on the blood cells and their clinical applications, particularly by means of bone marrow culture. *Acta Haemat. Jap.*, **19**, 406

*HIRAKI, K. and OFUJI, T. (1957) Maladie des radiations études hématologiques utilisant la culture de tissus de moelle osseuse. Recherches hématologiques effectuées sur des malades exposés aux radiations de la bombe à hydrogène dans la région de l'atoll de Bikini et étude sur les effets des rayons X et du P^{32} sur des cultures de tissu médullaire de lapin. (Haematological studies of radiation sickness using bone marrow culture. Haematological research into the effects of exposure to radiations of the hydrogen bomb in the area of the Bikini atoll and studies of the effects of X-rays and P^{32} on rabbit bone marrow cultures). *Sang*, 861

HIRAKI, K., OFUJI, T. and SUNAMI, H. (1956) The method of tissue culture (mainly of bone marrow) and a simple method of observing living tissue. *Acta Med. Okayama*, **10**, 99

*HIRAKI, K., OFUJI, T. and WATARI, Z. (1956) Observation of various living blood cells by tissue culture of the bone marrow. *Acta Med. Okayama*, **10**, 110

*HIRAKI, K., SUNAMI, H. and NISHISHITA, H. (1959) Influences of various hormones on the megakaryocyte in bone-marrow tissue culture. *Acta Med. Okayama*, **13**, 189

*HIRAKI, K., WATANABE, S. and KOTSUKA, T. (1960) Basic studies on the fluorochrominized bone marrow tissue culture and its application to the diagnosis of leukemia. *Acta Haemat. Jap.*, **23**, 609

HIRSCHFELD, H. (1927) Zuchtungsversuche mit leukämischen Blut.

(Experiments in culture of leukaemic blood). *Folia Haemat.*, *Leipzig*, **34**, 39

HIRSCHFELD, H. and KLEE-RAWIDOWICZ, E. (1928) Untersuchungen über die Genese der Blutmakrophagen und verwandter Zellformen und ihr Verhalten in der *in-vitro*-Kultur. I. Mitteilung normales und leukämisches Menschenblut. (Studies on the genesis of the blood macrophages and related cells, and their behaviour in tissue culture. I. Normal and leukaemic human blood). *Z. Krebsforsch.*, **27**, 167

*HOMBURG, C. J., BOS, C. J., DE BRUYN, W. M. and EMMELOT, P. (1961) Glycolytic and respiratory properties of malignant and non-malignant lymphoblasts cultured *in vitro*. *Cancer Res.*, **21**, 353

HOOGSTRATEN, J. (1949) The nature of leukaemia and the leukaemic cell. *Ph.D. Thesis*, Cambridge University

HOOGSTRATEN, J. (1950) *Proc. 3rd Congr. Int. Soc. Haemat.*, *Cambridge*, (Grune and Stratton, New York), p. 244

*HUEPER, W. C. and RUSSELL, M. (1932) Some immunological aspects of leukaemia. *Arch. Intern. Med.*, **49**, 113

*HUGHES, A. F. and FELL, H. B. (1949) Studies on abnormal mitosis induced in chick tissue cultures by mustard gas. *Qu. J. Micr. Sci.*, **90**, 37

HUMBLE, J. G. (1962) Personal communication

HUMBLE, J. G., JAYNE, W. H. W. and PULVERTAFT, R. J. V. (1956) Biological interaction between lymphocytes and other cells. *Brit. J. Haemat.*, **2**, 283

*HUMBLE, J. G., JAYNE, W. H. W., PULVERTAFT, R. J. V. and WILSON, C. W. (1954) The effect of irradiation on human lymphocytes. *J. Fac. Radiol.*, **5**, 227.

HUNGERFORD, D. A., DONNELLY, A. J., NOWELL, P. C. and BECK, S. (1959) The chromosome constitution of a human phenotypic intersex. *Amer. J. Hum. Genet.*, **11**, 215

INGERBRIGTSEN, R. (1912) The influence of heat on different sera as culture media for growing tissues. *J. Exp. Med.*, **15**, 397

INGRAM, V. M. and STRETTON, A. O. W. (1959) Genetic basis of the thalassaemia diseases. *Nature*, **184**, 1903

INGLE, D. and MASON, H. L. (1938) Subcutaneous administration of cortin compounds in solid form to the rat. *Proc. Soc. Exp. Biol.*, **39**, 154

ISRAELS, M. C. G. (1940a) The culture *in vitro* of leucocytes from human bone marrow. *J. Path. Bact.*, **50**, 145

ISRAELS, M. C. G. (1940b) The nature of human leukaemia: evidence from the culture of bone marrow cells *in vitro*. *J. Path. Bact.*, **51**, 235

ITANO, H. A. (1953) Qualitative and quantitative control of adult hemoglobin synthesis. A multiple allele hypthesis. *Amer. J. Hum. Genet.*, **5**, 34

IZAK, G. and NELKEN, D. (1957) Studies in thrombopoiesis. II. Thrombocytopoiesis *in vitro* from the bone marrow of patients with idiopathic thrombocytopenic purpura. *Blood*, **12**, 520

IZAK, G., NELKEN, D. and GUREVITCH, J. (1957) Studies on thrombopoiesis. I. Thrombocytopoiesis *in vitro*: experiments with animal and normal human material. *Blood*, **12**, 507

*JACOBSON, W. (1952) The role of the leuconostoc citrovorum factor (L.C.F.) in cell division and the mode of action of folic acid antagonists in normal and leukaemic cells. *J. Path. Bact.*, **64**, 245

JACOBSON, W. (1954a) The mode of action of folic acid antagonists and the function of the leuconostoc citrovorum factor; in *Ciba Foundation Symposium, Chemistry and Biology of Pteridines* (Churchill, London), p. 329

JACOBSON, W. (1954b) The function of leuconostoc citrovorum factor in cell division and the inactivation of aminopterin. *J. Physiol.*, **123**, 618

*JACOBSON, W. and CATHIE, I. A. B. (1960) The inactivation of folic acid antagonists by normal and leukaemic cells. *Biochem. Pharmacol.*, **5**, 130

*JACOBSON, W. and WILLIAMS, S. M. (1945) Observations on the anti-pernicious anaemia factor: with a suggested method for testing liver extracts in the laboratory. *J. Path. Bact.*, **57**, 101

JAGO, Margaret (1961) The radiosensitivity of normal and leukaemic human blood lymphocytes. *Clin. Radiol.*, **12**, 59

JENEY, A. (1932) Weitere Beobachtungen an blutbildenden Organen in Gewebekulturen. (Further observations on haemopoietic organs in tissue cultures). *Virchows Arch.*, **287**, 373

JOHNSTON, A. W., FERGUSON-SMITH, M. A., HANDMAKER, S. D., JONES, H. W. and JONES, G. S. (1961) The triple-X syndrome. *Brit. Med. J.*, ii, 1046

JOLLY, J. (1903) Sur la durée de la vie et de la multiplication des cellules animales en dehors de l'organisme. (On the longevity and multiplication of animal cells outside the organism). *C.R. Soc. Biol.*, **55**, 1266

KATZENSTEIN, R. (1931)   Unterzuchungen über die Umwandlungs-fahrigkeit der Lymphzellen. (Investigations into the transformation capacity of lymph cells). *Virchows Arch.*, **281**, 172

KIELER, J. (1955) Personal communication

*KIELER, J. (1955) The effect of explantation on the transplantability of leukaemic cells. *Rev. Hémat.*, **10**, 516

KIELER, J. (1957) Cultivation of leukemic cells in the Cartesian diver; in REBUCK, BETHELL and MONTO'S *The Leukemias: Etiology, Pathophysiology, and Treatment* (Academic Press, New York), p. 215

KIELER, J. (1959) Personal communication

*KIELER, J., BICZ, W. and MOSBECH, J. (1962)   Influence of CO_2 tension on leukaemia cell metabolism. *Proc. 8th Congr. Eur. Soc. Haemat., Vienna 1961* (Karger, Basel and New York, 1962)

KIELER, J. and KIELER, E. (1954) The effects of A–methopterin on sensitive and resistant leukaemic cells *in vitro. Cancer Res.*, **14**, 428

KLEIN, R. (1959)   Demonstration par la microcinématographie en contraste de phase de la transformation reversible des lymphocytes en macrophages *in vitro*. Rôle des lymphocytes et macrophages dans le méchanisme de l'immunité. (Phase contrast microcinematographic demonstration of the *in vitro* reversible transformation between lymphocytes and macrophages. Role of lymphocytes and macrophages in the mechanism of immunity). *C.R. Soc. Biol.*, **153**, 545

KRIPPAEHNE, M. L. and OSGOOD, E. E. (1955)   Studies of the influence of cortisone and hydrocortisone on human leukocytes in culture and in eosinophilic leukemia. *Acta Haemat.*, **13**, 145

LACASSAGNE, A. and GRICOUROFF, G. (1927)   De l'actions des radiations sur les leucocytes du sang, étudiée au moyen de la méthode des cultures. (Actions of radiations on the leucocytes of the blood, studied through culture method). *J. Radiol. Electrol.*, **11**, 573

LAJTHA, L. G. (1950)   An inhibitory factor in pernicious anaemia serum. *Clin. Sci.*, **9**, 287

LAJTHA, L. G. (1952)   Culture of human bone marrow *in vitro*. The reversibility between normoblastic and megaloblastic series of cells. *J. Clin. Path.*, **5**, 67

LAJTHA, L. G. (1957)   Bone marrow cell metabolism. *Physiol. Rev.*, **37**, 50

LAJTHA, L. G. (1959)   On DNA labelling in the study of the dynamics of bone marrow cell populations; in Stohlhman's *Kinetics of cellular proliferation* (Grune and Stratton, New York), p. 173

LAJTHA, L. G. (1960)   Radiation effects on nucleic acid metabolism.

In Chargaff-Davidson's *The nucleic acids* (Academic Press, New York, 1960), **3**, 527

*LAJTHA, L. G. (1960) Bone marrow culture. *Meth. Med. Res.*, **8**, 12

*LAJTHA, L. G. (1961) The effect of ionizing radiations and tumour-chemotherapeutic agents on the bone marrow. *Progr. Biophys.*, **11**, 80

LAJTHA, L. G., ELLIS, F. and OLIVER, R. (1953) Isotope uptake of individual cells: uptake of S^{35} sulphate by human bone marrow cells *in vitro*. *Brit. J. Cancer*, **7**, 401

LAJTHA, L. G., NOYES, W. D. and OLIVER, R. (1959) On the utilization of 5–amino–4–imidazole carboxamide (AICA) for purine synthesis by bone marrow cells *in vitro*. *Exp. Cell Res.*, **16**, 471

LAJTHA, L. G. and OLIVER, R. (1960a) Autoradiographic study on the radiosensitivity of normal and abnormal cells. *Proc. Int, Congr. Radiol., Munich* (Thieme, Stuttgart), p. 577

LAJTHA, L. G. and OLIVER, R. (1960b) Studies on the kinetics of erythropoiesis: a model of the erythron. In Ciba Foundation Symposium. *Haemopoiesis. Cell production and its regulation* (Churchill, London), p. 289

LAJTHA, L. G., OLIVER, R., BERRY, R. and NOYES, W. D. (1958) Mechanism of radiation effect on the process of synthesis of deoxyribonucleic acid. *Nature*, **182**, 1789

LAJTHA, L. G., OLIVER, R. and ELLIS, F. (1954) Incorporation of ^{32}P and adenine ^{14}C into DNA by human bone marrow cells *in vitro*. *Brit. J. Cancer*, **8**, 367

LAJTHA, L. G., OLIVER, R., KUMATORI, T. and ELLIS, F. (1958) On the mechanism of radiation effect on DNA synthesis. *Radiat. Res.*, **8**, 1

LAJTHA, L. G. and SUIT, H. D. (1955) Uptake of radioactive iron (^{59}Fe) by nucleated red cells *in vitro*. *Brit. J. Haemat.*, **1**, 55

LAPIN, J. and HORONICK, A. (1956) Ameboid motility of human leukocytes. *Blood*, **11**, 225

*LASZLO, J., LANDAU, B., WIGHT, K. and BURK, D. (1958) The effect of glucose analogs on the metabolism of human leukemic cells. *J. Nat. Cancer Inst.*, **21**, 475

LASZLO, J., STENGLE, J., WIGHT, K. and BURK, D. (1958) Effects of chemotherapeutic agents on metabolism of human acute leukaemic cells *in vitro*. *Proc. Soc. Exp. Biol.*, **97**, 127

LEIGHTON, J. (1951) A sponge matrix method for tissue culture. Formation of organised aggregates of cells *in vitro*. *J. Nat. Cancer Inst.*, **12**, 545

*LEIGHTON, J. (1955) Test tube and flask cultures. In *An introduction to cell and tissue culture* (Burgess, Minneapolis), p. 33

LENNOX, B. (1961) Chromosomes for beginners. *Lancet*, *i*, 1046

LEWIS, Margaret R. (1925) The formation of macrophages, epithelioid cells and giant cells from leucocytes in incubated blood. *Amer. J. Path.*, **1**, 91

LEWIS, Margaret R. (1926) A study of the mononuclears of the frog's blood *in vitro*. *Arch. exp. Zellforsch.*, **2**, 228

LEWIS, Margaret R. and LEWIS, W. H. (1911a) The growth of embryonic chick tissues in artificial media, agar and bouillon. *Bull. Johns Hopk. Hosp.*, **22**, 126

LEWIS, Margaret R. and LEWIS, W. H. (1911b) The cultivation of tissues from chick embryos in solutions of NaCl, $CaCl_2$, KCl and $NaHCO_3$. *Anat. Rec.*, **5**, 277

LEWIS, W. H. (1927) Migration of neutrophilic leucocytes. *Arch. exp. Zellforsch.*, **4**, 442

*LEWIS, W. H. and LEWIS, Margaret R. (1938) Studies on white blood cells. *Carn. Inst.*, *Washington*, **501**, 369

*LI, J. G. and OSGOOD, E. E. (1949) A method for the rapid separation of leukocytes and nucleated erythrocytes from blood or marrow with a phytohemagglutinin from red beans (*Phaseolis vulgaris*). *Blood*, **4**, 670

LOEB, L. (1897) Über die Entstehung von Bindegewebe, Leucocyten und roten Blutkorperchen aus Epithel und über eine Methode isolierte Gewebsteile zu zuchten. (On the development of connective tissue, leucocytes and red corpuscles from epithelium and on a new method of cultivating isolated fragments of tissue). (Max Stern and Co. Chicago)

*LOEB, L. (1901) On the growth of epithelium. *J. Amer. Med. Ass.*, **37**, 1024

*LOEB, L. (1902) On the growth of epithelium in agar and blood serum in the living body. *J. Med. Res.*, **8**, 109

*LOEB, L. and FLEISCHER, M. S. (1911) Über die Bedentung des Sanerstoffs für das Wuchstum der Gewebe von Sangeterieren. (The importance of oxygen for the growth of mammalian tissues). *Biochem. Z.*, **36**, 98

MCCULLOCH, E. A. and PARKER, R. C. (1956) Continuous cultivation of cells of hemic origin. *Canad. Cancer Conf.* (Academic Press, New York), **2**, 152

MCCULLOCH, E. A., PARKER, R. C. and WIGHTMAN, K. J. R. (1956) Continous cultivation of cells derived from hemic cells of man and pure strain mice. *Proc. Amer. Ass. Cancer. Res.*, **2**, 132

*MCINTYRE, O. R. and EBAUGH, F. G. Jr. (1962) The effect of

phytohemagglutinin on leukocyte cultures as measured by P^{32} incorporation in the DNA, RNA, and acid soluble fractions. *Blood*, **19**, 443

*MACKINNEY, A. A. jr., STOHLMAN, F. jr. and BRECHER, G. (1962) The kinetics of cell proliferation in cultures of human peripheral blood. *Blood*, **19**, 349

*MADDEN, R. E. and BURK, D. (1961) Production of viable single cell suspensions from solid tumors. *J. Nat. Cancer Inst.*, **27**, 841

MARCUS, P. I., CIECIURA, S. J. and PUCK, T. T. (1956) Clonal growth *in vitro* of epithelial cells from normal human tissues. *J. Exp. Med.*, **104**, 615

MARKSON, J. L. and RENNIE, J. B. (1956) The anaemia of chronic renal insufficiency; the effect of serum from azotemic patients on the maturation of normoblasts in suspension cultures. *Scot. Med. J.*, **1**, 320

MARSHALL, R. and CAPON, B. (1961) Factor stimulating cell division in cultured leucocytes. *Lancet*, **ii**, 103

MAS y MAGRO, F. (1932) Untersuchungen über die normale Erythropoese und zur Frage der Dedifferenzierung der Erythroblasten-*in-vitro*-Kulturen des Knockenmarks bei den Säugetieren und den Vögen. (Investigations on normal erythropoiesis and the question of differentiation of erythroblasts *in vitro* bone marrow cultures of mammals and birds). *Arch. exp. Zellforsch.*, **12**, 432

MATOTH, Y., BIEZUNSKI, Naomi and SZABO, G. (1958) Effect of sera from patients with anoxia on the proliferative activity of human erythropoietic tissue *in vitro*. *J. Lab. Clin. Med.*, **51**, 420

*MATOTH, Yehuda and KAUFMANN, Lily (1962) Mitotic activity *in vitro* of erythroblasts previously exposed to erythropoietin. *Blood*, **20**, 165.

*MAUER, A. M. and FISHER, Virginia (1962) Comparison of the proliferative capacity of acute leukaemia cells in bone marrow and blood. *Nature*, **193**, 1085

*MAXIMOW, A. (1923) Untersuchungen über Blut und Bindegewebe. IX. Über die experimentelle Erzeugung von myeloiden Zellen in Kulturen des lymphoiden Gewebes. (On the experimental production of myeloid cells in cultures of lymphoid tissue). *Arch. mikr. Anat.*, **97**, 314

MAXIMOW, A. (1927) Development of non-granular leucocytes (lymphocytes and monocytes) into polyblasts (macrophages) and fibroblasts *in vitro*. *Proc. Soc. Exp. Biol.*, **24**, 570

MAXIMOW, A. (1928) Über die Entstehung von argyrophiler und kollagener Fasern *in vitro*. (On the development of argyrophil and collagen fibres *in vitro*). *Zbl. allg. Path. u. path. Anat.*, **43**, 145

MAXIMOW, A. (1929)   Über die Entwicklung argyrophiler und kollagener Fasern in Kulturen von erwachsenem Säugetiergewebe. (On the development of argyrophil and collagenous fibres in cultures of adult mammalian tissue). *Z. micr.-anat. Forsch.*, **17**, 625

MAXIMOW, A. (1932) The lymphocytes and plasma cells. In Cowdry's *Special Cytology*, 2nd Ed., **2**, 601 (Hoeben, New York)

MEIER, R., POSERN, E. and WEITZMANN, G. (1937a)   Über das Verhalten der blutbilden Organe der erwachsemen Menschem *in vitro*. (On the behaviour of blood-forming organs of the adult human *in vitro*). *Virchows Arch.*, **299**, 316

MEIER, R., POSERN, E. and WEITZMANN, G. (1937b)   Das Wachstum menschlichen Lymphogranuloms *in vitro*. (The growth of a human lymphogranuloma *in vitro*). *Virchows Arch.*, **299**, 329

*MIRAS, C., LEWIS, G. and MANTZOS, J. (1961)   *In vitro* incorporation of sodium acetate-1-C^{14} into leukocyte lipids of normal and leukaemic subjects as a function of incubation time. *Nucl.-Med. (Stuttg.)*, **2**, 165

MONTGOMERY, H. and HORWITZ, O. (1950)   Oxygen tension of tissues by the polarographic method. I. Introduction: oxygen tension and blood flow of the skin of human extremities. *J. Clin. Invest.*, **29**, 1120

MOORHEAD, P. S., NOWELL, P. C., MELLMAN, W. J., BATIPPS, D. M. and HUNGERFORD, D. A. (1960)   Chromosome preparations of leukocytes cultured from human peripheral blood. *Exp. Cell Res.*, **20**, 613

MORGAN, J. F., MORTON, H. J. and PARKER, R. C. (1950)   Nutrition of animal cells in tissue culture. I. Initial studies on a synthetic medium. *Proc. Soc. Exp. Biol.*, **73**, 1

*MURRAY, M. R. and KOPECH, G. (1953)   A bibliography of the research in tissue culture (Academic Press, New York)

*NEUMAN, R. E. and MCCOY, T. A. (1955)   A simple assay procedure for materials and conditions in tissue culture. *Exp. Cell Res.*, **9**, 212

NORRIS, E. R. and MAJNARICH, J. J. (1948a) Effects of xanthopterin on cell proliferation in bone marrow cultures. *Amer. J. Physiol.*, **152**, 175

NORRIS, E. R. and MAJNARICH, J. J. (1948b)   Effect of normal blood and blood serum from neoplastic disease on cell proliferation in bone marrow cultures. *Amer. J. Physiol.*, **153**, 483

*NORRIS, E. R. and MAJNARICH, J. J. (1949)   Cell proliferation accelerating and inhibiting substances in normal and cancer blood and urine. *Proc. Soc. Exp. Biol.*, **70**, 229

NOSSAL, G. (1962) Personal communication

*NOTAKE, K., ICHIKAWA, Y., HANAOKA, M. and AMANO, S. (1961) On a new long-term *in vitro* culture of normal and leukemic lymphocytes with special reference to a favourable simultaneous proliferation of leukemic virus and host-cell. *Acta Haemat. Jap.*, **24**, 591

NOWELL, P. C. (1960a) Differentiation of human leukemic leukocytes in tissue culture. *Exp. Cell Res.*, **19**, 267

NOWELL, P. C. (1960b) Phytohemagglutinin. An initiator of mitosis in cultures of normal human leukocytes. *Cancer Res.*, **20**, 462

NOWELL, P. C. (1961) Personal communication

*NOWELL, P. C. (1961) Inhibition of human leukocyte mitosis by prednisolone *in vitro*. *Cancer Res.*, **21**, 1518

NOWELL, P. C. and HUNGERFORD, D. A. (1960) Chromosome studies on normal and leukemic human leukocytes. *J. Nat. Cancer Inst.*, **25**, 85

ODOM, Retha and REISNER, E. H. (1959) Culture of bone marrow on dextrose agar. *Clin. Res. Proc.*, **7**, 14

OSGOOD, E. E. (1937) Culture of human marrow. Length of life of the neutrophils and basophils of normal blood as determined by comparative cultures of blood and sternal marrow from healthy persons. *J. Amer. Med. Ass.*, **109**, 933

*OSGOOD, E. E. (1938) Culture of human marrow. An improved apparatus for large scale culture. *Amer. J. Med. Sci.*, **195**, 141

OSGOOD, E. E. (1939a) Marrow cultures. In *A symposium on the blood and blood-forming organs* (The University of Wisconsin Press, Madison), p. 219

*OSGOOD, E. E. (1939b) The cultivation of human marrow as an aid in the evaluation of therapeutic agents. Studies of sulfanilamide and related compounds. *J. Lab. Clin. Med.*, **24**, 954

OSGOOD, E. E. (1940) Effects of irradiation on leukemic cells in marrow cultures. *Proc. Soc. Exp. Biol.*, **45**, 131

OSGOOD, E. E. (1955) Tissue culture in the study of leukocytic functions. *Ann. N.Y. Acad. Sci.*, **59**, 806

OSGOOD, E. E. (1957) Observations on human leukemic cells in culture. In Rebuck, Bethell and Monto's *The Leukemias: Etiology, pathophysiology, and treatment*, (Academic Press, New York), p. 227

*OSGOOD, E. E. (1959) Blood cell survival in tissue cultures. *Ann. N.Y. Acad. Sci.*, **77**, 777

OSGOOD, E. E. and BRACHER, G. J. (1939) Culture of human marrow: studies of the effects of Roentgen-rays. *Ann. Intern. Med.*, **13**, 563

OSGOOD, E. E. and BROOKE, J. H. (1955) Continuous tissue culture of leukocytes from human leukemic bloods by application of 'gradient' principles. *Blood*, **10**, 1010

*OSGOOD, E. E. and BROOKE, J. H. (1958) Methods developed for culture of human leukocytes. *Meth. Med. Res.*, **7**, 156

OSGOOD, E. E. and BROWNLEE, I. E. (1936) Culture of human bone marrow. A simple method for multiple cultures. *J. Amer. Med. Ass.*, **107**, 123

OSGOOD, E. E. and BROWNLEE, I. E. (1937) Culture of human marrow. Details of a simple method. *J. Amer. Med. Ass.*, **108**, 1793

OSGOOD, E. E. and CHU, I. T. (1948) The effect of urethane on the nuclear morphology of cells of the granulocyte series as observed in marrow cultures and leukemic blood. *Blood*, **3**, 911

OSGOOD, E. E. and KRIPPAEHNE, M. L. (1955) The gradient tissue culture method. *Exp. Cell Res.*, **9**, 116–127

*OSGOOD, E. E. and KRIPPAEHNE, M. L. (1955) Comparison of the life span of leukemic and non-leukemic neutrophils. *Acta Haemat.*, **13**, 153.

OSGOOD, E. E., LI, J. G., TIVEY, H., DUERST, M. L. and SEAMAN, A. J. (1951) Growth of human leukemic leucocytes *in vitro* and *in vivo* as measured by uptake of P^{32} in DNA. *Science*, **114**, 95

OSGOOD, E. E. and MUSCOVITZ, A. N. (1936) Culture of human bone marrow. Preliminary report. *J. Amer. Med. Ass.*, **106**, 1888

*OWEN, O. V. H., GEY, M. K. and GEY, G. O. (1953) A new medium for the cultivation of mammalian cells in agitated fluid medium. *Amer. Ass. Cancer Res.*, **1**, 41

OWEN, O. V. H., GEY, M. K. and GEY, G. O. (1954) Growth of cells in agitated fluid medium. *Ann. N.Y. Acad. Sci.*, **58**, 1039

PALMER, C. G., LIVERGOOD, D., WARREN, A. K., SIMPSON, P. J. and JOHNSON, I. S. (1960) The action of Vincaleukoblastine on mitosis *in vitro*. *Exp. Cell Res.*, **20**, 198

PARKER, F. and RHOADS, C. P. (1928) Some observations on incubated leukemic bloods. *Amer. J. Path.*, **4**, 167

PARKER, R. C. (1961) Methods of tissue culture (Hoeber, New York), 3rd Edition

*PAUL, J. (1957) A perfusion chamber for cinemicrographic studies. *Qu. J. Micr. Sci.*, **98**, 279

PAUL, J. (1960) Cell and tissue culture (Livingstone, Edinburgh and London), 2nd Edition

PEARMAIN, G., LYCETTE, R. R. and FITZGERALD, P. H. (1963) Tuberculin-induced mitosis in peripheral blood leucocytes. *Lancet, i*, 637

*PHILLIPS, H. J. and ANDREWS, R. V. (1959) Some protective solutions for tissue-cultured cells. *Exp. Cell Res.*, **16**, 678

PHILLIPS, H. J. and FELDHAUS, R. J. (1956) Respiration and glycolysis of Earle's strain L cells. *Proc. Soc. Exp. Biol.*, **92**, 478

PHILLIPS, H. J. and MCCARTHY, M. L. (1956) Oxygen uptake and lactate formation of HeLa cells. *Proc. Soc. Exp. Biol.*, **93**, 573

PHILLIPS, H. J. and TERRYBERRY, J. E. (1957) Counting actively metabolizing tissue cultured cells. *Exp. Cell Res.*, **13**, 341

PIERCE, Mila (1932) Cultures of leukemic blood leukocytes. *Arch. Path.*, **14**, 295

PILATI, L. and PINELLI, L. (1936) Cultura *in vitro* di sangue leucemico (leucemia linfatica cronica). (*In vitro* culture of leukaemic blood (chronic lymphatic leukaemia). *Boll. Soc. Ital. Biol. Sper.*, **11**, 449

*PISCIOTTA, A. V. and KALDAHL, Joyce (1962) Studies on agranulocytosis. IV. Effects of chlorpromazine on nucleic acid synthesis of bone marrow cells *in vitro*. *Blood*, **20**, 364

PLUM, C. M. (1947a) *In vitro* study of bone marrow. I. A method for marrow culture. *Blood*, Special Issue no. 1, 33

PLUM, C. M. (1947b) *In vitro* study of bone marrow. II. Studies of erythropoiesis. *Blood*, Special Issue no. 1, 42

*PLUM, C. M. and CLEMMESEN, J. (1952) *In vitro* study of bone marrow. V. Erythropoiesis of bone marrow from cases of pernicious anemia and leukosis. *Acta Med. Scand.*, **143**, 237

*POGO, B. G. T. and MOORE, A. E. (1961) Effect of folic acid on *in vitro* uptake of labeled thymidine by leukemic cells. *Proc. Soc. Exp. Biol.*, **108**, 409

*POLÁK, H. and POLÁKOVÁ, K. (1956) The influence of transfusion on the amoeboid activity of leucocytes. Indirect evidence of a factor increasing the motility of leucocytes. *Acta Haemat.*, **16**, 385

*POMERAT, C. M. (1951) Perfusion chamber. *Meth. Med. Res.*, **4**, 275

POMERAT, C. M., LEFEBER, C. G. and SMITH, M.C.D. (1954) Quantitative ciné analysis of cell organoid activity. *Ann. N.Y. Acad. Sci.*, **58**, 1311

PORTER, K. R., CLAUDE, A. and FULLAM, E. F. (1945) A study of tissue culture cells by electron microscopy. Methods and preliminary observations. *J. Exp. Med.*, **81**, 233

*POWSNER, E. R. and BERMAN, L. (1959) Correlation of radioactive hemin formation with morphologic alterations in cultures of human bone marrow. *Blood*, **14**, 1213

*PRUSOFF, W. H., LAJTHA, L. G. and WELCH, A. D. (1956) Effect of desoxyriboside and 6–azalthymine (Azathymidine) on biosynthesis of deoxyribonucleic acid by bone marrow and neoplastic cells (*in vitro*). *Biochim. Biophys. Acta*, **20**, 209

PUCK, T. T. (1958) Action of radiation on mammalian cells. III. Relationship between reproductive death and induction of chromosome anomalies by X-irradiation of euploid human cells *in vitro*. *Proc. Nat. Acad. Sci., Washington*, **44**, 772

PUCK, T. T., CIECIURA, S. J. and FISHER, H. W. (1957) Clonal growth *in vitro* of human cells with fibroblastic morphology. Comparison of growth and genetic characteristics of single epithelioid and fibroblast-like cells from a variety of human organs. *J. Exp. Med.*, **106**, 145

PUCK, T. T. and MARCUS, P. I. (1956) Action of X-rays on mammalian cells. *J. Exp. Med.*, **103**, 653

PUCK, T. T., MARCUS, P. I. and CIECIURA, S. J. (1956) Clonal growth of mammalian cells *in vitro*. Growth characteristics of colonies from single HeLa cells with and without a *feeder* layer. *J. Exp. Med.*, **103**, 273

PULVERTAFT, R. J. V. (1958) The effect of reduced oxygen tension on platelet formation *in vitro*. *J. Clin. Path.*, **11**, 535

PULVERTAFT, R. J. V. (1959) Cellular associations in normal and abnormal lymphocytes. *Proc. Roy. Soc. Med.*, **52**, 315

PULVERTAFT, R. J. V., HAYNES, J. A. and GROVES, J. T. (1956) Perspex slides for roller culture of human cells. *Exp. Cell Res.*, **11**, 99

PULVERTAFT, R. J. V. and HUMBLE, J. G. (1956) Culture de moelle osseuse sur lames tournantes. (Culture of bone marrow on rotating slides). *Rev. Hémat.*, **11**, 349

PULVERTAFT, R. J. V. and HUMBLE, J. G. (1960) The bone marrow in leukaemia. *Acta Haemat.*, **24**, 68

*PULVERTAFT, R. J. V. and HUMBLE, J. G. (1962) Intracellular phase of existence of lymphocytes. *Nature*, **194**, 194

PULVERTAFT, R. J. V. and JAYNE, W. H. W. (1953) Agar cultures of exudates. *Ann. Roy. Coll. Surg. Engl.*, **12**, 161

PULVERTAFT, R. J. V. and WEISS, L. (1957) The identification of living malignant cells in exudates. *J. Clin. Path.*, **10**, 390

PULVERTAFT, R. J. V., WILSON, C. W. and JAYNE, H. (1953) The effect on lymphocytes of ionising radiation. *Nature*, **171**, 1157

*PUNNETT, T., PUNNETT, Hope H. and KAUFMANN, B. N.   (1962) Preparation of a crude human leucocyte growth factor from *Phaseolis vulgaris*. *Lancet*, i, 1359

*RABSON, A. L., LEGALLAIS, F. and BARON, S. (1958) Adaption to serum-free medium by a phagocytic cell strain derived from a murine lymphoma. *Nature*, **181**, 1343

RACHMILEWITZ, M. and ROSIN, A. (1943) Studies on bone marrow *in vitro*. I. The cellular pattern and behaviour of explanted bone marrow. *Amer. J. Med. Sci.*, **206**, 17

RACHMILEWITZ, M. and ROSIN, A. (1944) Studies on bone marrow *in vitro*. II. The effect of hemoglobin and red cell stromata in explanted bone marrow. *Amer. J. Med., Sci.*, **208**, 193

RASSMUSSEN, H. (1933) Über das Verhalten von Knockenmark in der Gewebeskultur. (On the behaviour of bone marrow in tissue culture). *Arch. exp. Zellforsch.*, **14**, 285

REEVES, D. L. (1934) A study of the *in vivo* and *in vitro* behaviour of the monocytes of the blood stream and connective tissue. *Bull. Johns Hopk. Hosp.*, **55**, 245

*REISNER, E. H. Jr. (1958) The nature and significance of megaloblastic blood formation. *Blood*, **13**, 313

REISNER, E. H. Jr. (1959) Tissue culture of bone marrow. *Ann. N.Y. Acad. Sci.*, **77**, 487

*RHOADS, C. P. and PARKER, F. (1928) Observation on incubated tissues and exudates. *Amer. J. Path.*, **4**, 375

RICH, A. R., WINTROBE, M. M. and LEWIS, M. R. (1939) The differentiation of myeloblasts from lymphoblasts by their manner of locomotion. *Bull. Johns Hokp. Hosp.*, **65**, 291

RICHTER, K. M. (1955) Studies on leukocytic secretory activity. *Ann. N.Y. Acad. Sci.*, **59**, 863

RICHTER, K. M. and WOODWARD, N. W. (1955) A versatile type of perfusion chamber for long-term maintenance and direct microscopic observation of tissues in culture. *Exp. Cell Res.*, **9**, 585

RIGAS, D. A. and OSGOOD, E. E. (1955) Purification and properties of the phytohemagglutinin of *Phaseolus vulgaris*. *J. Biol. Chem.*, **212**, 607

*RIMINGTON, C. (1958) Biosynthesis of haemoglobin. *Brit. Med. Bull.*, **15**, 19

*RINALDINI, L. M. (1953) A quantitative method of cell culture. *J. Physiol.*, **123**, 20

RINALDINI, L. M. (1959) An improved method for the isolation and quantitative cultivation of embryonic cells. *Exp. Cell Res.*, **16**, 477

ROSE, G. (1954) A separable and multipurpose tissue culture chamber. *Texas Rep. Biol. Med.*, **12**, 1074

ROSE, G. (1955) A variant pinocytic cell (V.P. cell) of Gey's strain HeLa selectively produced and stimulated by human serum nutrients. *Texas Rep. Biol. Med.*, **13**, 475

*ROSE, G. (1957) Special uses of the multipurpose tissue culture chamber. *Texas Rep. Biol. Med.*, **15**, 310

ROSE, G. G., POMERAT, C. M., SHINDLER, T. O. and TRUNNELL, J. B. (1958) A cellophane-strip technique for culturing tissue in multipurpose culture chambers. *J. Biophys. Biochem. Cytol.*, **4**, 761

ROSSI, V., DIENA, F. and SACCHETTI, C. (1957) Demonstration of specific and non-specific agglutinogens in the normal bone marrow erythroblasts. *Experientia*, **13**, 440

ROTHFELS, K. H., AXELRAD, A. A., SIMINOVITCH, L., MCCULLOCH, E. A. and PARKER, R. C. (1959) The origin of altered cell lines from mouse, monkey, and man, as indicated by chromosome and transplantation studies. *Canad. Cancer Conf.*, **3**, 189

RUSZNYÁK, S., LÖWINGER, S. and LAJTHA, L. G. (1947) Maturation of megaloblasts in bone marrow cultures. *Nature*, **160**, 757

RUSZNYÁK, S., LÖWINGER, S. and LAJTHA, L. G. (1948) The factor in pernicious serum which inhibits the maturation of red blood cells. *Hung. Acta Med.*, **1**, 9

*SABIN, F. R. (1923) Studies of living human blood cells. *Bull. Johns Hopk. Hosp.*, **34**, 277

SABIN, F. R., AUSTRIAN, C. R., CUNNINGHAM, R. S. and DOAN, C. A. (1924) Studies on the maturation of myeloblasts into myelocytes and on amitotic cell division in the peripheral blood in subacute myeloblastic leukemia. *J. Exp. Med.*, **40**, 845

SACCHETTI, C. (1956) Physiopathologie des érythroblastes dans l'anémie des azotémies chroniques. (Physiopathology of erythroblasts in the anaemia of chronic uraemia). *Acta Haemat.*, **9**, 97

SACCHETTI, C. and BIANCHINI, E. (1953a) Action directe de S.T.H. sur les activités de la moelle osseuse humaine normale. (Direct effect of somatropin on the activity of normal human bone marrow). *Sang*, **24**, 344

SACCHETTI, C. and BIANCHINI, E. (1953b) Attività biologiche del midollo osseo nella leucemia mieloide cronica. I. Proliferazione ed evoluzione dei granuloblasti. II. Proliferazione e maturazione degli erithroblasti. (Biological activity of chronic myeloid leukaemia bone marrow. I. Proliferation and evolution of myeloblasts. II. Proliferation and maturation of the erythroblasts). *Boll. Soc. Ital. Biol. Sper.*, **29**, 1285

SACCHETTI, C. and BIANCHINI, E. (1955) Activité mitotique du noyau et maturation cytoplasmatique des mégacariocytes au cours de différents syndromes. (Mitotic activity of the nucleus and maturation of the cytoplasm of megakaryocytes in different syndromes). *Rev. Hémat.*, **10**, 538

*SACCHETTI, C., DIENA, F. and ROSSI, V. (1958) Comportamento degli eritroblasti nell'anemia emolitica acquisita. (Behaviour of erythroblasts in acquired haemolytic anaemia). *Haematologica*, **42**, 895

SACCHETTI, C. and PERREIRA, F. (1952) Le attività biologiche dei megaloblasti nell'anemia perniciosa e l'influenza della vitamina B_{12} applicata direttamente *in vitro*. (The biological activity of megalo-blasts in pernicious anaemia and the influence of vitamin B_{12} when applied directly *in vitro*). *Haematologica*, **36**, 1109

SACCHETTI, C., ROSSI, V. and DIENA, F. (1958) Behaviour of erythroblasts *in vitro* in sera from cases of acquired haemolytic anaemia. *Brit. J. Haemat.*, **4**, 416

SACCHETTI, C. and SALVIDIO, E. (1957) The biological activities of bone marrow granulopoiesis in experimental leucopenias. *Acta Haemat.*, **17**, 210

SALERA, V. and TAMBURINO, G. (1953) Studio dell'attività proli-ferativa dei granuloblasti. Richerche sul midollo osseo umano normale. (Studies on the proliferative activity of the granuloblasts. Research of normal human bone marrow). *Haematologica*, **37**, 1135

SALIS, H. (1948) Erythrophagocytosis in bone marrow culture with relation to antagonism of pteroylglutamic acid. *Proc. Soc. Exp. Biol.*, **68**, 382

SANDBERG, A. A., KOEPF, G. R., CROSSWHITE, L. H. and HAUSCHKA, T. S. (1960) The chromosome constitution of human marrow in various developmental and blood disorders. *Amer. J. Hum. Genet.*, **12**, 231

SANFORD, K. K., EARLE, W. R., EVANS, V. J., WALTZ, H. K. and SHANNON, J. E. (1950) The measurement of proliferation of tissue cultures by enumeration of cell nuclei. *J. Nat. Cancer Inst.*, **11**, 773

SANFORD, K. K., WALTZ, H. K., SHANNON, J. E., EARLE, W. R. and EVANS, V. J. (1952) The effect of ultrafiltrates and residues of horse serum and chick-embryo extract on proliferation of cells *in vitro. J. Nat. Cancer Inst.*, **13**, 121

*SATO, G., FISHER, H. W. and PUCK, T. T. (1957) Molecular growth requirements of single mammalian cells. *Science*, **126**, 961

*SCHENCK, D. M. and MOSKOWITZ, M. (1958) Method for isolating single cells and preparations of clones from human bone marrow cultures. *Proc. Soc. Exp. Biol.*, **99**, 30

SCHERER, W. F. (1955) (a) The laboratory: equipment and supplies; (b) Glassware and its cleaning; (c) Tissue extracts and derivatives. In *An introduction to cell and tissue culture*, (Burgess, Minneapolis), pp. 1, 2 and 11

K

*SCHINDLER, R., DAY, Margaret and FISHER, G. A. (1959) Culture of neoplastic mast cells and their synthesis of 5–hydroxytryptamine and histamine *in vitro. Cancer Res.*, **19**, 47

SCHREK, R. (1946a) Studies *in vitro* on the physiology of cells. Factors affecting the delayed cytocidal action of X-rays. *J. Cell. Comp. Physiol.*, **28**, 277

SCHREK, R. (1946b) Studies *in vitro* on cellular physiology. The effect of X-rays on the survival of cells. *Radiology*, **46**, 395

SCHREK, R. (1948) A comparison of the reaction of cells to nitrogen mustard and X-rays. *Acta Un. Int. Cancr.*, **6**, 848

SCHREK, R. (1949) Cytotoxic action of hormones of the adrenal cortex according to the method of unstained cell counts. *Endocrinology*,**45**,317

SCHREK, R. (1958a) Slide-chamber method to measure sensitivity of cells to toxic agents. *Arch. Path.*, **66**, 569

SCHREK, R. (1958b) *In vitro* sensitivity of normal human lymphocytes to X-rays and radiomimetic agents. *J. Lab. Clin. Med.*, **51**, 904

SCHREK, R. (1963) Motility of normal and leukemic human lymphocytes. *J. Lab. Z Clin. Med.*, **61**, 34

SCHREK, R., FRIEDMAN, I. A. and LEITHOLD, L. (1958) Variability of the *in vitro* sensitivity of human leukemic lymphocytes to X-rays and chemotherapeutic agents. *J. Nat. Cancer Inst.*, **20**, 1037

SCHROEDER, L. R., GURNEY, C. W. and WACKMAN, Nancy (1958) Assay of erythropoietin in bone marrow suspension. *Nature*, **181**, 1537

SCHULTZE, M. J. S. (1865) Ein heizbarer Objecttisch und seine Verwendung bei Untersuchungen des Blutes. (A heatable microscope stage and its application to examination of the blood). *Arch. mikr. Anat.*, **1**, 1

*SCOTT, J. L. (1962) Human leukocyte metabolism *in vitro*. I. Incorporation of adenine–8–C^{14} and formate–C^{14} into the nucleic acids of leukemic leukocytes. *J. Clin. Invest.*, **41**, 67

SHAFFER, B. M. (1956) Selective destruction of mesenchyme in tissue culture by the toxin of Clostridium welchii Type A. *Nature*, **178**, 1404

*SHAFFER, B. M. (1956) The culture of organs from the embryonic chick on cellulose-acetate fabric. *Exp. Cell Res.*, **11**, 244

SHARP, J., FEINMANN, E. L. and WILKINSON, J. F. (1952) A method of enumeration of individual elements. *Biometrics*, **8**, 105

SILBERBERG, M. and VOIT, K. (1931) Untersuchungen über die Unwandlung der forblasen Blutzellen bei lymphatischer Leukaemie. (Investigations on the transformation of the white blood corpuscles in lymphatic leukaemia). *Dtsch. Arch. klin. Med.*, **171**, 110

SIMINOVITCH, L., GRAHAM, A. F., LESLEY, S. M., and NEVILL, Ann (1957) Propagation of L strain mouse cells in suspension. *Exp. Cell Res.*, **12**, 299

SIMONS, J. W. I. M. (1962) The application of pure fibrinogen solutions in tissue culture. *Exp. Cell Res.*, **27**, 339

SMITH, D. R. (1952) The value of *in vitro* culture techniques in haematology. *M.D. thesis*, University of Cambridge

SMYTHE, H. F. (1914) A new medium for the cultivation of chick tissue *in vitro* with some additions to the technic. *J. Med. Res.*, **31**, 255

SPADAFINA, L. (1935) Contributo allo studio della cultura *in vitro* di modollo osseo. (Contribution to the study of culture of bone marrow *in vitro*). *Arch. exp. Zellforsch.*, **17**, 43

STEWART, D. C. and KIRK, P. L. (1954) The liquid medium in tissue culture. *Biol. Rev.*, **29**, 119

STOCK, C. C., BIESELE, J. J., BURCHENAL, J. H., KARNOFSKY, D. A., MOORE, A. E. and SUGIURA, K. (1950) Folic acid analogs and experimental tumors. *Ann. N.Y. Acad. Sci.*, **52**, 1360

STRANGEWAYS, T. S. P. and FELL, H. B. (1926) Experimental studies on the differentiation of embryonic tissues growing *in vivo* and *in vitro*. I. The development of the undifferentiated limb-bud (a) when subcutaneously grafted into the post-embryonic chick, and (b) when cultured *in vitro*. *Proc. Roy. Soc. Biol.*, **99**, 340

SUIT, H. D., LAJTHA, L. G., OLIVER, R. and ELLIS, F. (1957) Studies on the ^{59}Fe uptake by normoblasts and the failure of X-irradiation to affect uptake. *Brit. J. Haemat.*, **3**, 165

SWAN, H. T., REISNER, E. H. Jr. and SILVERMAN, M. (1955) The effect of various metabolites on the growth of marrow cells *in vitro*. *Blood*, **10**, 735

*SWEZY, O. (1915) Egg albumen as a culture medium for chick tissue. *Biol. Bull.*, **28**, 47

*SYKES, J. A., DMOCHOWSKI, L., SHULLENBERGER, C. C. and HOWE, C. D. (1962) Tissue culture studies on human leukemia and malignant lymphoma. *Cancer Res.*, **22**, 21

*TANZER, J. (1960) Culture de cellules à partir du sang humain suivant les techniques d'Osgood. (Culture of human blood cells by techniques of Osgood). *Rev. Hémat.*, **15**, 250

THIERY, J. P. and BESSIS, M. (1956a) Cytologie sanguine. La génèse des plaquettes sanguines à partir des mégacaryocytes observée sur la cellule vivant. (Cytology of blood. The formation of blood platelets by segmentation from megakaryocytes observed in the living cell). *C.R. Acad. Sci.*, **242**, 290

THIERY, J. P. and BESSIS, M. (1956b) Mécanisme de la plaquettogénèse. Étude *in vitro* par la microcinématographie. (Mechanism of platelet production. Study *in vitro* with microcinematography). *Rev. Hémat.*, **11**, 162

THOMAS, E. D. (1955) *In vitro* studies of erythropoiesis. I. The effect of normal serum on heme synthesis and oxygen consumption by bone marrow. *Blood*, **10**, 600

*THOMAS, E. D. (1955) *In vitro* studies of erythropoiesis. II. The effect of anoxia on heme synthesis. *Blood*, **10**, 612

THOMAS, E. D. and LOCHTE, H. L. Jr. (1957)   Desoxyribonucleic acid synthesis by bone marrow cells *in vitro*. *Blood*, **12**, 1086

THOMAS, M. C. (1956) The growth and development of human leuco-cytes *in vitro* with particular reference to leukaemic cells. *M.Sc. thesis*, Cambridge University

THOMPSON, R. B. (1950)   Addisonian pernicious anemia. Confirm-atory evidence of a factor inhibiting erythropoiesis. *Clin. Sci.*, **9**, 281

THOMPSON, R. B. (1952) Observations on the effect of vitamin B^{12}, liver extract, folic acid and thymidine on the maturation of megalo-blasts in culture. *Blood*, **7**, 522

*TIMOFEEVSKY, A. D. (1928) Über Leukozytenkulturen des Menschen-blutes *in vitro*. (On leucocyte cultures from human blood *in vitro*). *Arch. exp. Zellforsch.*, **6**, 259–264

TIMOFEEVSKY, A. D., and BENEVOLENSKAYA, S. W. (1926)   Ex-plantationsversuche von weissen Blutkorperchen mit Tuberkelbazillen. (Explant experiment of white blood corpuscles with tubercule bacilli). *Arch. exp. Zellforsch.*, **2**, 31

TIMOFEEVSKY, A. D. and BENEVOLENSKAYA, S. W. (1927)   Pros-pektive Potenzen des Myeloblasten auf Grund von Explantations-versuchen. (Prospective potentialities of myeloblasts based on explan-tation experiments). *Virchows Arch.*, **263**, 719

TIMOFEEVSKY, A. D. and BENEVOLENSKAYA, S. W. (1929)   Neue Beobachtungen an lymphoiden Zellen der myeloiden und lympatischen Leukämie in Explantations-versuchen. (New observations on lymphoid cells of myeloid and lymphatic leukaemias in explant experiments). *Arch. exp. Zellforsch.*, **8**, 1

*TOY, B. L. and BARDAWIL, W. A. (1958) A simple plastic perfusion chamber for continuous maintenance and cinematography of tissue cultures. *Exp. Cell Res.*, **14**, 97

TRINCAO, C., PARREIRA, F., GOUVEIA, E. and FRANCO, A. (1952) Action du fer sur la moelle osseuse des malades d'ankylostomiase. II. Influence du fer sur la maturation *in vitro* des érythroblastes. (Action of iron on the bone marrow in ankylostomiasis. II. Influence of iron on the *in vitro* maturation of erythroblasts). *Rev. Hémat.*, **7**, 580

TROWELL, O. A. (1952) The culture of lymph nodes *in vitro*. *Exp. Cell Res.*, **3**, 79

*TROWELL, O. A. (1952) The sensitivity of lymphocytes to ionizing radiation. *J. Path. Bact.*, **64,** 687

TROWELL, O. A. (1953) The action of cortisone on lymphocytes *in vitro. J. Physiol.*, **119,** 274

*TROWELL, O. A. (1953) The effect of environmental factors on the radio-sensitivity of lymph nodes cultured *in vitro. Brit. J. Radiol.*, **26,** 302

TROWELL, O. A. (1954) A modified technique for organ culture *in vitro. Exp. Cell Res.*, **6,** 246

*TROWELL, O. A. (1955) Experiments on lymph nodes cultured *in vitro. Ann. N.Y. Acad. Sci.*, **59,** 1066

TROWELL, O. A. (1956) Personal communication

TROWELL, O. A. (1958) Personal communication

*TROWELL, O. A. (1958) Some properties of lymphocytes *in vivo* and *in vitro. Ann. N.Y. Acad. Sci.*, **73,** 105

TROWELL, O. A. (1959) The culture of mature organs in a synthetic medium. *Exp. Cell Res.*, **16,** 118

TROWELL, O. A. (1960) The cytocidal action of mitotic poisons on lymphocytes *in vitro. Biochem. Pharmacol.*, **5,** 53

TROWELL, O. A. (1961a) Personal communication

*TROWELL, O. A. (1961b) La culture organotypique. Associations et dissociations d'organes en culture *in vitro*. (Problems in the maintenance of mature organs *in vitro*). *Colloques Internationaux du Centre National de la Recherche Scientifique, No.* **101,** 237

TYRODE, M. V. (1910) The mode of action of some purgative salts. *Arch. Int. Pharmacodyn.*, **20,** 205

UMBREIT, W. W., BURRIS, R. H. and STAUFFER, J. F. (1948) Manometric techniques and related methods for the study of tissue metabolism (Burgess, Minneapolis)

VAN DEN BERGHE, L., GAVRILOV, W. and BOBKOFF, G. (1938) Observations sur la moelle osseuse en culture de tissus. (Observations on bone marrow in tissue culture). *C.R. Soc. Biol.*, **129,** 51

VAN HERWERDEN, M. A. (1918) Expériences de culture de la moelle osseuse en dehors de l'organisme. (Experiments on the culture of bone marrow outside the organism). *Arch. Néerl. Physiol.*, **2,** 711

*VAS, Magdalene R., BAIN, Barbara and LOWENSTEIN, L. (1962) The effect of chloramphenicol in human bone marrow cultures. *Blood*, **20,** 424

136   BLOOD AND BONE MARROW CELL CULTURE

VASILIU, T. and STOICA, V. (1929) Culture *in vitro* du sang du lapin. (Culture *in vitro* of rabbit's blood). *C.R. Soc. Biol.*, **100**, 691

VERATTI, E. (1928) Cultura *in vitro* di sangue umano normale e patologico. (*In vitro* culture of normal and pathological human blood). *Haematologica*, **9**, 89

*VON BOLL, I. and GANSSEN, O. (1962) Die Mitosedauer der Paraleukoblasten. (The mitosis of paraleucoblasts). *Acta Haemat.*, **27**, 229

WALLBACH, G. (1936) Forms of appearance of cultivated human leukocytes in different diseases of the leukopoietic apparatus. *Arch. exp. Zellforsch.*, **18**, 315

*WALSH, R. J., THOMAS, E. D., CHOW, S. K., FLUHARTY, R. G., and FINCH, C. A. (1949) Iron metabolism. I. Heme synthesis *in vitro* by immature erythrocytes. *Science*, **110**, 396

*WARBURG, O. and KRIPPAHL, G. (1960) Further development of manometric methods. *J. Nat. Cancer Inst.*, **24**, 51

WAYMOUTH, Charity (1951) Measurements of growth by nucleic acid determinations. *Meth. Med. Res.*, **4**, 225

*WAYMOUTH, Charity (1955) Simple nutrient solutions for animal cells. *Texas Rep. Biol. Med.*, **13**, 522

*WAYMOUTH, Charity (1956) A serum-free nutrient solution sustaining rapid and continuous proliferation of strain L (Earle) mouse cells. *J. Nat. Cancer Inst.*, **17**, 315

WAYMOUTH, Charity (1959) Rapid proliferation of sublines of NCTC clone 929 (strain L) mouse cells in a simple chemically defined medium (MB 752/1). *J. Nat. Cancer Inst.*, **22**, 1003

WAYMOUTH, Charity (1960) Effects of some metal salts on the rate and efficiency of growth of cells of NCTC clone 929 (strain L) in synthetic media. *Excerpta med.*, Sect. I, 352

WEIL, G. C. (1912) Some observations on the cultivation of tissues *in vitro*. *J. Med. Res.*, **26**, 159

*WEISS, L. (1959) Studies on cellular adhesion in tissue culture. I. The effect of serum. *Exp. Cell Res.*, **17**, 499

*WEISS, L. (1959) Studies on cellular adhesion in tissue culture. II. The adhesion of cells to gel surfaces. *Exp. Cell Res.*, **17**, 508

WEISS, L. P. and FAWCETT, D. W. (1953) Cytochemical observations on chicken monocytes, macrophages and giant cells in tissue culture. *J. Histochem. Cytochem.*, **1**, 47

WELLS, B. B. and KENDALL, E. C. (1940) The influence of corticosterone and C^{17} hydroxydehydrocorticosterone (Compound E) on somatic growth. *Proc. Mayo Clin.*, **15**, 324

WERTHEMAN, A. (1932) Über die Umwandlungsfähigkeit der Blutzellen, insbesondere in Gewebskulturen. (Regarding the ability of blood cells to undergo transformations, especially in tissue culture). *Schweiz. Med. Wchnschr.*, **13**, 749

*WESTWOOD, J. C. N., MACPHERSON, I. A. and TITMUSS, D. H. J. (1957) Transformation of normal cells in tissue culture: its significance relative to malignancy and virus vaccine production. *Brit. J. Exp. Path.*, **38**, 138

WHITBY, L. (1951) Whither clinical pathology? Trends and opportunities. *J. Clin. Path.*, **4**, 129

WHITBY, L. and BRITTON, C. (1957) Disorders of the blood. (Churchill, London) 8th Ed.

WHITE, P. R. (1946) Cultivation of animal tissues *in vitro* in nutrients of precisely known constitution. *Growth*, **10**, 231

WHITE, P. R. (1949) Prolonged survival of excised animal tissues *in vitro* in nutrients of known constitution. *J. Cell Comp. Physiol.*, **34**, 221

WHITE, P. R. (1954) The cultivation of animal and plant cells (Ronald Press Co., New York)

WHITFIELD, J. R. and RIXON, R. H. (1960) Radiation resistant derivative of L strain mouse cells. *Exp. Cell Res.*, **19**, 531

*WHITFIELD, J. R. and RIXON, R. H. (1960) Some properties of radiation resistant derivates of L strain mouse cells. *Exp. Cell Res.*, **20**, 242

*WILLMER, E. N. (1933a) Studies on the growth of tissues *in vitro*. I. Some effects of the mechanical properties of the medium on the growth of chick heart fibroblasts. *J. Exp. Biol.*, **10**, 317

WILLMER, E. N. (1933b) Studies on the growth of tissues *in vitro*. II. An analysis of the growth of chick heart fibroblasts in a hanging drop of fluid medium. *J. Exp. Biol.*, **10**, 323

WILLMER, E. N. (1933c) Studies on the growth of tissues *in vitro*. III. An analysis of the growth of chick heart fibroblasts in flask cultures in plasma coagulum. *J. Exp. Biol.*, **10**, 340

*WOLFE, E. and HAFFEN, K. (1952) Sur une méthode de culture d'organes embryonnaires *in vitro*. (On a method of culture of embryonic organs *in vitro*). *Texas Rep. Biol. Med.*, **10**, 463

WOODLIFF, H. J. (1958a) Glass substrate cultures of human blood and bone marrow cells. *Exp. Cell Res.*, **14**, 368

WOODLIFF, H. J. (1958b) A further use of Rose's tissue culture chamber. *Texas Rep. Biol. Med.*, **16**, 380

WOODLIFF, H. J. (1960) Effect of 6–Mercaptopurine on the net *in vitro* gas production of sensitive and resistant L 1210 mouse leukaemia cells. *Nature*, **187**, 156

WOODLIFF, H. J. (1961) Serum agar cultures of blood and bone marrow cells. *Acta Haemat.*, **25**, 300

WOODLIFF, H. J. (1962) Blood and bone marrow cell cultures. *Ph.D. Thesis*, Cambridge University

WOODLIFF, H. J. and DAVIS, J. M. G. (1960) The effect of Amethopterin and 6–Mercaptopurine on the pattern of oxygen tension measurements of the fluid phase of serum agar cultures of bone marrow flecks. *Nature*, **185**, 477

WOODLIFF, H. J. (1963) The effect of antimetabolites on the respiration of leukemic mouse cells. *Blood*, **22**, 199

WRIGHT, J. H. (1906) The origin and nature of blood platelets. *Boston Med. Surg. J.*, **154**, 643

*YOUNGER, J. S. (1954) Monolayer tissue cultures. I. Preparation and standardization of suspensions of trypsin-dispersed monkey kidney cells. *Proc. Soc. Exp. Biol.*, **85**, 202

*YUNIS, Adel A. and HARRINGTON, W. J. (1960) Patterns of inhibition of chloramphenicol of nucleic acid synthesis in human bone marrow and leukemic cells. *J. Lab. Clin. Med.*, **56**, 831

*ZUBROD, G., FERREBEE, J., HOLLAENDER, A. and CONGDON, C. C. (1962) Co-chairmen – Symposium: Blood-bone marrow tissue culture and cell separation. *Blood*, **20**, 100

Index